THE *Map* WORKBOOK

THE COMPANION GUIDE TO CREATING YOUR DREAM LIFE

BONI LONNSBURRY

Inner Art, Inc.
1750 30th Street, Suite 543
Boulder, CO 80301

www.innerartinc.com

Editor: Bryna René, www.wordsbyaphrodite.com.
Cover design: theBookdesigners, Bryna René
Interior graphics: Devon Gibbs/Dreamstime stock images
Interior layout and design: Bryna René

Ordering Information

Quantity sales. Special discounts are available on quantity purchases by corporations, associations, and others. For details, please contact the publisher at the address above.

Publisher's Cataloging-In-Publication Data

Lonnsburry, Boni,

    The Map Workbook: The Companion Guide to Creating Your Dream Life / Boni Lonnsburry.
    p. cm.

    ISBN13: 978-1-941322-09-3
    ISBN10: 1-941322-09-3

1. New Thought / 2. Self-Realization / 3. Success. / 4. Joy. / 5. Optimism / 6. Metaphysics.
I. Title.

For Brandon and Brett,

who taught me to dream the impossible.

TABLE OF Contents

PART TWO: CREATION SESSIONS

PART THREE: TROUBLESHOOTING

INTRODUCTION

HOW TO USE THIS BOOK

YOU CREATE YOUR OWN REALITY. NO FINE PRINT.

NO EXCEPTIONS. NO ASTERISKS.

I can't imagine anyone reading those words and not being excited!

Did you get that? Are you letting that in?

This workbook is intended to serve as a companion to *The Map*. It's the compass to your treasure map, if you will. Throughout these pages you will find exercises, journaling prompts, checklists, and Q&A worksheets to help you get the most out of the information presented in *The Map*. Some of the exercises in this workbook were created directly from *The Map*, others are brand new. Work with these tools in the way that best serves you. Remember, creating your reality can be fun!

WHAT IS THE MAP?

The Map is a step-by-step guide on how to create. It will help you build a dream, whether you know what you want or not. From financial abundance to a loving relationship, a youthful body to a happy family, The Map can help you create everything you desire.

If you follow it, The Map can not only help you to discover and clarify your dreams, it can help you to make them manifest in your world—in vivid, delightful, synchronistic, and fulfilling ways.

WHAT CAN THE MAP DO FOR YOU?

With *The Map* and the tools in this workbook, you will follow a clear, concise, step-by-step process to make your dreams real. You will learn how to tell if it's working, and what to do if it doesn't work. You'll learn to draw help into your life, and weed out the things that aren't so helpful.

I spent many years perfecting what I know about reality creation. Now, you can reap the rewards of my perseverance. It won't always be easy, but it will definitely be worth it.

I know you can do this. After all, creating the life of your dreams is what you came here to do. There's no time like the present, so let's get started!

THE *Map* WORKBOOK

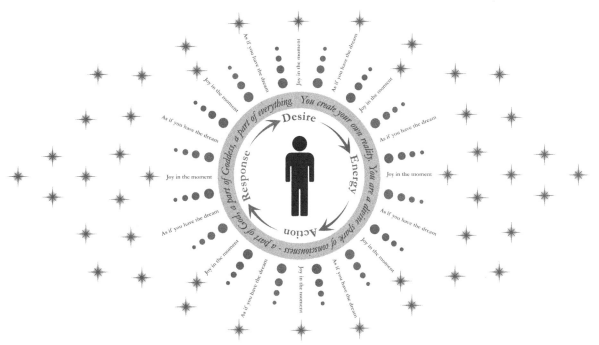

PART ONE

CREATION STEPS

CHAPTER ONE

THE ART OF CONSCIOUS CREATION

"You were born with potential. You were born with goodness and trust. You were born with ideals and dreams. You were born with greatness. You were born with wings. You are not meant for crawling, so don't. You have wings. Learn to use them, and fly!"

- Rumi

All the joy, all the love, and all the successes in your life are your creations. All the misery, all the scarcity, and all the struggles are also your creations. Okay, maybe you're not conscious of how you have created them—yet—but they are still your creations. And if they are your creations, the difficulties in your life aren't because of your parents, or spouse, or children, or the economy, or the politicians, or your body, or your boss.

Consciously creating your reality means you can take one hundred percent responsibility for all areas of your life and your world. You can change your world *substantively.*

As long as you are alive, you will be creating your reality, because this is the way the world works. If you are not consciously creating it, you will be *unconsciously* creating it.

When you're ready to start creating consciously, it's important to know that things will not bring you the essence—the wonderful, positive feeling state—that you want to achieve. Rather, the essence will bring you the things. So, even if you lose all the things in your life through unintentional miscreation, you can always create them again, simply by calling forth the wonderful feeling state from which creation energy springs.

Now *that* is absolute empowerment!

CREATION STEP *One*

PURCHASE A NOTEBOOK TO USE AS YOUR CREATION JOURNAL, OR START A NEW DOCUMENT ON YOUR COMPUTER AND NAME IT "CREATION JOURNAL."

You will use this journal as a supplement to the writing space in this workbook to document your intentions, techniques, actions, beliefs, and signs as you do this work.

You may include successes in this journal, or use a separate file or journal to document your successes. Or you can purchase a Creation Journal or Success Journal specifically for this purpose at LiveALifeYouLove.com.

CREATION JOURNAL CREATED/PURCHASED?

DATE: *Artu* 9/11/21

Revisit this journal often as a way to regain a sense of power, confidence, and expectation. It is very effective to bring these energies to new dreams and visions. You accomplish this by simply reading about your past processes and successes and feeling a sense of accomplishment and power before you do any techniques for your new dreams.

CREATION STEP *Two*

WHAT DOES "CREATING YOUR REALITY" MEAN TO YOU?

Creating the life I desire - living my dreams and giving back to those around me.

On a scale of one to ten, one being, *"I don't believe it is possible to create one's own reality at all,"* and ten being, *"I am certain every human on this planet is creating their own reality, and I have the absolute ability to consciously create everything in my own life,"* where are you?

1   2   3   4   5   6   7   (8)   9   10

Where would you like to be in one year?

I weigh 150 lbs & I walk 5 miles a day Pain free. I have opened up my shop. I am living my dream.

In five years?

I am healthier than I have ever been. My on-line business allows us to be digital nomads. At 67! I feel 36! I look 46! My shop grew — we travel, the Center opened. We have classes in Art, Yoga, we love our life. Meditation, Tai Chi — it's wonderful. The Center generates more money than I could have dreamed. I have over a million $'s saved for retirement — but who needs to retire!

CREATION STEP *Three*

WRITE OUT ALL THE THINGS, EVENTS, AND RELATIONSHIPS IN YOUR LIFE FOR WHICH YOU ARE NOW TAKING FULL, UNEQUIVOCAL RESPONSIBILITY—BOTH GOOD AND BAD.

As you write out each item, say aloud, "I take full responsibility for creating this!"

POSITIVE

By Chewy!
Troy!
~~Family~~ Relationships
Our home
Our abundance
~~Health~~
My relationships
My studio

CHALLENGING

GPR Job
Back Issues
Health
Weight
Desire for more
~~Health~~
My relationships!
My relationship w/ health
Knee issues

PART OF CREATING YOUR OWN REALITY IS TAKING RESPONSIBILITY FOR EVERYTHING YOU'VE CREATED IN YOUR LIFE UP UNTIL NOW.

What thoughts and feelings arose for you during the last exercise?

It was harder than I thought. The challenging items were more related to me, (my body, health) and therefore sad that they were challenging.

& I realized they (the items) could be ~~were~~ reversed from side to side.

Was it harder for you to take full responsibility for the "Positive" items, or the "Challenging" ones?

The challenging ones

Were there any items for which you were reluctant to take full responsibility?

Why? What would it say about you if you owned these things completely?

Its hard to say that I am responsible for making myself sick.
And that I am responsible for not liking my job. It is making me rethink how I approach my job and what I need to do to make it good.

10

CREATION STEP *Four*

INTEND TO GET WHERE YOU WANT TO BE WITH REGARD TO YOUR POWER TO CONSCIOUSLY CREATE 100% OF YOUR REALITY.

Write your intention for conscious creation below.

*I am my creator.
I create everything in my reality.
I am creating my life of my dreams & I am grateful!*

Everything is possible!

A POSSIBLE INTENTION:

"I intend to know and fully believe—beyond a shadow of a doubt—that I create everything in my reality and that I can create a life of my dreams."

Once you are satisfied with your intention, read it aloud several times. Say it like you mean it, because the Universe recognizes intention and feeling!

CHAPTER TWO

FOLLOW THE MAP
TO A LIFE YOU LOVE

"The man who moved a mountain is the one who started taking away the small stones."

~ Old Chinese Proverb

There is a more real you who chose to come to this planet. That "you" wanted to experience certain things in this lifetime. Before you were born, you chose your parents, your siblings, the time and place of your birth, and some of your childhood experiences. Obviously, you also chose to forget just about everything you knew before you were born.

You forgot:

- That you are a God-being.

- That you chose to incarnate on a planet of free will.

- That "reality" is an illusion.

- That you are connected to everything, everywhere.

- That you create it all!

SOME THINGS TO REMEMBER ABOUT REALITY CREATION

- Conscious creation is a whole new way of life for almost every one of us. It took decades to get to where we are with the old way of life. Learning a new one takes some time and effort— but the results are worth it.

- Time lag is the time it takes for something to manifest in time and space. A thought and feeling you had two weeks ago could manifest in your reality today. Time lag makes people believe what they see, instead of realizing they see what they believe (and think and feel).

- There are very few exceptions to the rule that we create our own reality. The rare exception is a mental or physical challenge you chose to be born with. Everything else (and sometimes even that) can be healed and changed.

CREATION STEP *One*

HOW IMPORTANT IS CREATING THE LIFE OF YOUR DREAMS TO YOU?

> **ON A SCALE OF 1 TO 10, RATE THE IMPORTANCE OF CREATING THE**
>
> **LIFE OF YOUR DREAMS, CONSCIOUSLY AND DELIBERATELY.**
>
> **1   2   3   4   5   6   7   8   9   (10)**

Why did you choose that rating? *There isn't anything more important! This is it. Its The lesson & The reason I am here.*

How much effort are you willing to put forth to create your dream life?

whatever it takes.

What hesitations, fears, and doubts do you have?
(Remember to release them when you're done writing!)

- I want to ensure I am specific or - be careful what you wish.
  I want to bring the correct thing into my life.

- I know this will work. There is a voice inside me which doubts it. It is tied to past experience. But I know that is fear.

RELEASE YOUR DOUBTS BY SAYING,

"I hereby release my hesitations, fears, and doubts about creating a life I love!"

CREATION STEP *Two*

"THERE IS A MORE 'REAL' YOU WHO CHOSE TO COME TO THIS
PLANET TO EXPERIENCE CERTAIN THINGS IN THIS LIFETIME."

How does this statement make you feel? Empowered? Doubtful?

Frightened? Joyous? Relieved? Something else? Write your feelings below.

*Somewhat sad that the real me has been
lost for so long. I understand why I have done
things the way I have (fear based responsibility) but
it does make me sad.*

*I want Julie Ann to be strong, empowered,
free, abundant, healthy & happy to be
giving energy to the planet.*

*I need to learn how to step out of this
life & into the next step in creating.*

When you're done writing, sit in meditation for a few minutes. Open to
this truth. Let it in. If you like, invite your higher self to join you and ask
them to help you get in touch with the more *real* you. Then, write your
feelings and thoughts again on the next page. Has anything shifted for
you? How?

My thoughts and feelings after meditating ...

IF
YOUR FIRST
MEDITATION
DIDN'T FULLY
EASE YOUR DOUBTS
AROUND YOUR
CHOICE TO COME
HERE IN THIS LIFETIME,
REPEAT IT DAILY UNTIL
YOU START TO FEEL A
SHIFT. WRITE ABOUT
EACH MEDITATION
EXPERIENCE IN
YOUR CREATION
JOURNAL.

CREATION STEP *Three*

TAKE FIVE MINUTES TO FEEL EXCITEMENT, JOY, AND PURE DELIGHT BECAUSE YOU WILL (FINALLY) BE LIVING THE LIFE OF YOUR DREAMS!

Imagine what your life will be like five years from now when all of your current dreams have become manifest. Write about this experience below.

I am so happy! Making this shift was everything I thought it would be — and I am living the life I've always dreamed of. Troy & I are thriving as a couple, our businesses are successful, I get to take Chewy to work, and life is good.

— I feel relieved that I 'got it'

CHAPTER THREE

WHO *ARE* YOU, REALLY?

"It is the creative potential itself in human beings that is the image of God."

~ Mary Daly

You are by your very nature, divine. You are a piece of God and Goddess and you have been given a gift: the ability to create.

Feeling regret about the past can stop you from letting in the true nature of your being. Forgive yourself. Realize that despite being a spark of the Divine, you are also human. You have made mistakes and you will make more. It doesn't make you any less divine.

Be open to the guidance, love, and assistance of your unseen friends. It will strengthen your flow, it will raise your resonance, and it will make all of your creations easier and more elegant. Because it is true. You are a piece of God, a piece of Goddess. And you are loved. Deeply, unequivocally, unconditionally loved.

CREATION STEP *One*

SIT WITH THE KNOWING THAT YOU ARE A GOD-BEING.

Don't just say the words, really feel it. What thoughts, emotions, fears, or doubts come up for you? Write your thoughts below.

If I am a God-being, how can I be so flawed.
God has so many labels & connotations stuck to it for me ... I start to turn off.
(I feel like I am a creator — which is the same)
I feel like I am trying to find a lost friend.

23

Now, set aside any fears or doubts that came up during the first part of this exercise. Ask yourself, "What if it's true that I am a God-being?" (By the way … It is!)

Then I feel like I've wasted a good deal of time.

I've only allowed myself to be me about 25% of the time —

If this gift of divinity has been bestowed upon you, can you think of anything more insulting than to ignore it? How can you honor your God-self and own who you really are, right now?

By being true to this, being true to me.

CREATION STEP

WORK WITH THE "PRE-SLEEP REQUEST"

Say the Pre-sleep Request (mentally or aloud) nightly for seven days.

Write down any meaningful dreams or insights during this time period.

THE PRE-SLEEP REQUEST

"Higher self ... please help me to see and own more of who I really am. Help me to remove whatever may be in the way of recognizing my divinity and the power and ability I have to create my reality. Please show me and guide me in gentle, loving, and easy ways, with harm to none. Thank you, higher self."

 DAY 1

 DAY 2

DAY 3

 DAY 4

 DAY 5

 DAY 6

 DAY 7

CREATION STEP *Three*

WRITE OUT ALL THE THINGS FOR WHICH YOU WOULD LIKE TO FORGIVE YOURSELF.

Part of owning your God-ness is forgiving yourself for past mistakes and experiences. Remember you don't have to forgive the actual act, but you can forgive why you did it—the place you were in, the pain you were holding, etc.

AS YOU COMPLETE EACH ITEM, SAY ALOUD, *"I forgive myself for _____. I am worthy of forgiveness. I am a divine God-being."*

I FORGIVE MYSELF FOR …

_____

_____

_____

_____

_____

_____

_____

_____

_____

_____

CREATION STEP *Four*

"BLENDING WITH YOUR HIGHER SELF" TECHNIQUE

Find a quiet place to sit or lie down where you will not be disturbed. Put on some soft music and get comfortable.

Say (mentally or aloud): "Higher self, I would like you to join me in this blending. Please make your presence and your love known to me. I seek to have a greater knowing of who I really am, and to open to my divinity and my God-given ability to create my reality. Please help me with these intentions with gentleness, love, joy, grace, and harm to none."

Gently close your eyes. Feel the presence of your higher self enveloping you in love. Allow the love to heal you, support you, and teach you. Open to the experience of knowing who you really are.

You may sense your higher self as a light, a warmth, or simply a loving presence. You may see your higher self in human form in your mind's eye, and they may come to lie or sit next to you. Or you may simply feel their presence. The way they look may change during the blending or over subsequent blendings or meditations. Trust yourself.

Spend five or ten minutes with your higher self. Let it be real!

When you're finished, write about your experience on the next page.

CREATION STEP FOUR, CONT.

{ Writing Space }

CREATION STEP *Five*

"YOUR NURTURING UNIVERSE" TECHNIQUE

Find a place to sit quietly. Put on some soft music and light a candle. Breathe deeply, allowing yourself to relax. Feel the air around you wrapping you in a gentle embrace of love.

Imagine that air around you forming a bubble … a bubble of light and love extending two feet beyond your body. Everything that enters this bubble seeks to love you. Everything that enters this bubble seeks to support you. This bubble is filled with nurturing love for you. It is the love of God, of Goddess. It is the love of the Divine seeking to connect with you and strengthen your knowing of its love for you. Now imagine the bubble expanding to the size of the room.

Then allow the bubble to expand to the size of your house. Imagine this entire house-sized bubble nurturing you, supporting you, loving you. Now let the bubble grow, and grow, and grow, until it's the size of your neighborhood, your city, your country. Let the bubble expand around the entire planet.

THIS IS YOUR WORLD. YOU GET TO CHOOSE IF IT IS THREATENING OR LOVING. IMAGINE HOW YOUR LIFE WOULD CHANGE IF THE WORLD WERE CONSPIRING TO SAY "YES" TO YOUR EVERY DREAM. IMAGINE HOW IT WOULD FEEL TO LIVE IN A WORLD WHERE EVERYWHERE YOU LOOKED YOU WERE MET WITH SUPPORT, LOVE, GUIDANCE, AND ACCEPTANCE.

Imagine how your life would change if the world were conspiring to say "Yes!" to your every dream. Imagine how it would feel to live in a world where, everywhere you looked, you were met with support, love, guidance, and acceptance.

This is your world. *You* get to choose whether it is threatening or loving—so choose loving!

30

CREATION STEP FIVE, CONT.

Sit for as long as you like in what is becoming your world. When you're finished, write about your experience below.

CHAPTER FOUR

CLARIFYING YOUR DREAM

"The imagination is a dream factory of which realities are a by-product"

~ Richard Wilkens

Every day requires you to stay conscious and put forth the flow to maintain what you've created. Every new dream requires you to follow The Map all over again.

Is it worth it? Heck, yeah!

You don't even have to know exactly what you want to create. You only have to know how you want to feel. And let's face it, everyone knows that they ultimately want to feel good.

DREAMS BEGIN WITH INTENTIONS

There are lots of ways to begin to dream, but the most effective and elegant way to begin a dream is with *intentions*.

Intentions are statements of, well, intent. Intent is strong, clear, and willed. Although we are talking about a dream or desire, the choice to turn that dream into an intention adds strength and commitment.

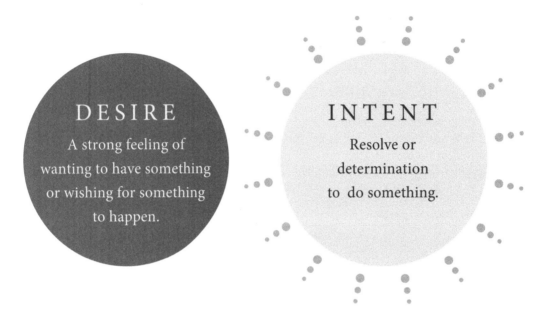

DESIRE
A strong feeling of wanting to have something or wishing for something to happen.

INTENT
Resolve or determination to do something.

Stating an intention turns the wish (desire) into a *commitment to create.*

Intentions mean business. They aren't wishy-washy. They tell your conscious and subconscious minds, "One way or another, I will create what I want!"

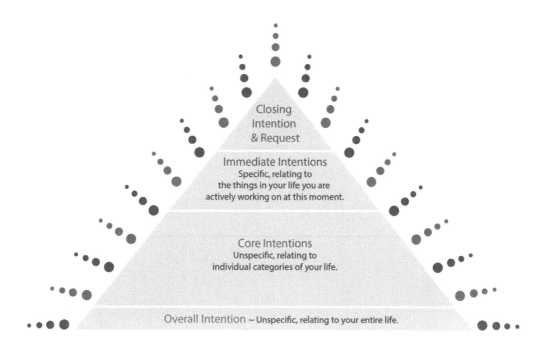

Closing
Intention
& Request

Immediate Intentions
Specific, relating to
the things in your life you are
actively working on at this moment.

Core Intentions
Unspecific, relating to
individual categories of your life.

Overall Intention ~ Unspecific, relating to your entire life.

THE INTENTION PYRAMID

Intentions are built from the bottom up—from your Overall Intention, to your Core Intentions, to your Immediate Intentions.

In the next section, you'll create your intentions one by one, for each area of your life. (If you need more writing space, use extra pages in your Creation Journal or on your computer.) Remember to refer to Chapter Four of *The Map* for specific instructions on how to create your most powerful and effective intentions.

CREATION STEP *One*

LET GO OF OLD, TIRED DREAMS

Are you carrying around old dreams from your child, adolescent, or young adult selves, or unhelpful dreams that no longer serve you? It might be time to let these dreams die.

Write them out in the space below (or in a document on your computer). As you write each dream, say, *"I release this dream, with love, from my conscious, subconscious, and unconscious minds."* Then, tear out this page (or print the page from your computer) and burn it, symbolically releasing all of your old dreams.

MY OLD DREAMS

Be sure to burn your list of old dreams in a safe place (like over the kitchen sink).

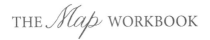

CREATION STEP ONE, CONT.

{ extra writing space }

CREATION STEP

OVERALL INTENTION

Your Overall Intention is the backbone of all your intentions. This is the bird's eye view of how you want your life to be.

Create your Overall Intention in the space below. Remember to write it as an experiential or feeling state—and be sure it feels wonderful to you!

MY OVERALL INTENTION

NEED HELP?
Review page 70 of The Map.

CREATION STEP *Three*

CORE INTENTIONS

Your Core Intentions address every category of your life. Most of the intentions you work with will be Core Intentions.

REMEMBER TO BE AS NON-SPECIFIC AS YOU CAN ABOUT HOW YOUR CORE INTENTIONS LOOK.

There are millions of possibilities—trust that the universe will deliver the best outcome for you!

Instead of focusing on the *things* you want, think about how you want to *feel* in each area of your life.

Write your Core Intentions for each category on the next page.

(For guidance, see pages 70-79 of *The Map*.)

REMEMBER, IF YOU'RE NOT SURE WHAT YOU WANT, YOU CAN BEGIN BY WRITING WHAT YOU DON'T WANT, AND REVERSING IT. (See page 65 of *The Map*.

CREATION STEP THREE, CONT.

MY CORE INTENTIONS

LOVING PARTNERSHIP INTENTIONS

OTHER RELATIONSHIP INTENTIONS
including children, friends, parents, coworkers, etc.

WORK INTENTIONS

PHYSICAL BODY INTENTIONS

PHYSICAL ENVIRONMENT INTENTIONS

SPIRITUAL INTENTIONS

CREATION STEP THREE, CONT.

MENTAL AND EMOTIONAL INTENTIONS

PLAY INTENTIONS

CREATIVE INTENTIONS

FINANCIAL INTENTIONS

EARTH AND HUMANITY INTENTIONS

FOR MORE
HELP WITH
CREATING
INTENTIONS, AND
TO SEE EXAMPLES
OF INTENTIONS IN
EACH CATEGORY,
SEE PAGES 82-103
OF *THE MAP*

COSMIC INTENTIONS

CREATION STEP *Four*

IMMEDIATE INTENTIONS

Your Immediate Intentions are the intentions for the projects and creations that are your top priority right now. When writing Immediate Intentions, it is appropriate (but not necessary) to be more specific.

MY IMMEDIATE INTENTIONS

NEED HELP?
*Review page 79
of The Map.*

{ extra writing space }

CREATION STEP *Five*

CLOSING INTENTION & REQUEST

This is where you turn to your unseen friends and ask for their energy, light and love. It's also where you open to the possibility that your unseen friends may have something even better in mind.

MY CLOSING INTENTION & REQUEST

SAMPLE CLOSING INTENTION & REQUEST

"I request and intend to receive help from all of my unseen friends to manifest all of my intentions even greater than stated, with harm to none."

CREATION STEP *Six*

HOW DID IT FEEL FOR YOU TO WRITE OUT AND CONSCIOUSLY MAP YOUR INTENTIONS?

Were any intentions more challenging than others to put down on paper?

Which intentions felt light and expansive? Which felt heavy or clumsy?

Write about your experience in the space below.

CREATION STEP *Seven*

REVIEW AND REFLECT

Over the course of the next several days and weeks, review your intentions at least twice daily (once in the morning and once before bed). Flow energy to them and through them. Read them aloud. Add to them. Strengthen them. Rewrite those which no longer feel expansive or authentic to you. Periodically write about your changing relationship to your intentions in the space below. Be sure to date your reflections so you can track your progress!

Reflection Date _____

If you run out of space in this workbook, add pages in a computer document or your Creation Journal.

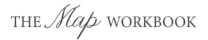
THE *Map* WORKBOOK

 Reflection Date _____

 Reflection Date _____

CREATION STEP SEVEN, CONT.

 Reflection Date _____

Reflection Date _____

 Reflection Date _____

 Reflection Date _____

CREATION STEP SEVEN, CONT.

Reflection Date _____

Reflection Date _____

CHAPTER FIVE

BRINGING YOUR DREAM TO LIFE!

"Look, and you will find it—what is unsought will go undetected."

~ Sophocles

Knowing you create your reality is not enough. If you want to manifest something consciously, you must flow energy towards your desire, and you must stop flowing energy away from that desire.

Imagine that you are a car. The fuel to get you to your destination (your desire) is energy (positive emotion). The more fuel you put in and convert to movement, the faster you can go.

But there's an opposing force, too. We'll call it "Anti-Fuel."

Negative energy neutralizes your fuel so it's powerless. And, if it's strong enough, it can propel you backwards, further away from the thing you want.

WHAT MAKES THE FLOW GROW?

* Thinking about *having* the thing you want.

* Feeling positive emotion (fuel) about having the thing you want.

WHAT STOPS THE FLOW?

* Thinking negative or doubtful thoughts about what you want.

* Feeling negative emotions about what you want.

Desire (circular text: You create your own reality. You are a divine spark of consciousness — a part of God, a part of Goddess, a part of everything.)

The exercises in this section are designed to help you uncover your "Anti-Fuel"—your flow-stoppers—and work to convert those energies to positive, flow-enhancing dream feeders.

Note that your flow-stoppers will not always appear alone. Sometimes, several flow-stoppers appear to be one emotion (e.g., disappointment and doubt).

Use the space on the following pages to uncover and work with your flow-stoppers. You may need to do these exercises more than once, over the course of several days or weeks. If you need more space, use pages in a computer document or your Creation Journal.

CREATION STEP One

UNCOVER YOUR FLOW-STOPPERS

FLOW-STOPPER 1: SELF-PITY

When was the last time you felt sorry for yourself?

What triggers self-pity for you?

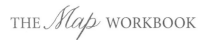

What benefit do you receive by feeling self-pity?

How do you think self-pity interferes with your power to consciously create?

What is your plan for the next time it happens?

FLOW-STOPPER 2: DOUBT

When was the last time you felt doubt (fleeting or persistent)?

If doubt is an issue for you, ask yourself if you hold any of these beliefs:

Y   N   It is impossible to consciously create our own reality.

Y   N   It is impossible to consciously create everything in my reality.

Y   N   Conscious reality creation is impossible for me.

Y   N   It is hard work to consciously create my reality.

Y   N   It is impossible to create _____ .

Y   N   I am not _____ enough to create what I desire.

If yes, use the belief-changing techniques in Chapter Six to change them to:

It is possible to consciously create our own reality.

It is possible to consciously create everything in my reality.

Conscious reality creation is possible for me.

It is very easy to consciously create my reality.

It is possible to create _____.

I am _____enough to create what I desire.

Belief changing techniques can be found on pages 181-189 of *The Map*

59

What benefit do you receive by feeling doubt?

How do you think doubt interferes with your power to consciously create?

What is your plan for the next time you experience fleeting doubt?

CREATION STEP ONE, CONT.

FLOW-STOPPER 3: FEAR

When was the last time you felt afraid?

What brings up fear for you?

Do you have beliefs that might be causing your fear?

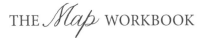

THE *Map* WORKBOOK

What benefit do you receive by feeling fearful?

How do you think fear interferes with your power to consciously create?

What do you plan to do the next time you become afraid?

FLOW-STOPPER 4: MARTYRDOM

When was the last time you felt overburdened, unappreciated, or like you gave too much?

What or who triggers your feelings of martyrdom?

What benefit do you receive by feeling martyred or self-sacrificing?

How does martyr energy interfere with your power to consciously create?

What do you plan to do the next time these feelings arise?

FLOW-STOPPER 5: CONTROL

When was the last time you felt like you needed to control someone, something, or a situation?

Are there certain areas of your life where you are more likely to try to control?

Do you hold any of these beliefs?

Y　　N　　I must control my reality in order to be safe.

Y　　N　　I must control others in order to be safe.

Y　　N　　I have to control to get what I want.

Y　　N　　If I don't control, I will be controlled.

Belief-changing techniques can be found on pages 181-189 of *The Map*.

If yes, use the belief-changing techniques in Chapter Six to change these beliefs to:

• I must create my own safety in order to be safe.

• I have to receive to get what I want.

• If I let go of control, I will be powerful.

How do you think the need to control interferes with your power to consciously create?

LATER IN THIS CHAPTER, YOU'LL FIND EXERCISES FOR WORKING WITH YOUR YOUNGER SELVES. USE THOSE TECHNIQUES TO GIVE THEM WHAT THEY WANT, SO THEIR ENERGY WON'T CAUSE YOU TO TRY TO CONTROL YOUR LIFE IN THE HERE AND NOW.

CREATION STEP ONE, CONT.

Sometimes it isn't the adult you who is afraid of what will happen if you lose control, but rather your child, adolescent, or young adult self. They may feel the need to control because they are afraid they won't be able to "do it right." What do your younger selves have to say about control?

What is your plan for the next time control issues surface?

CREATION STEP ONE, CONT.

{ extra writing space }

CREATION STEP ONE, CONT.

FLOW-STOPPER 6: IMPATIENCE

When was the last time you felt impatient?

What triggers impatience for you?

Do any beliefs underlie your impatience? (For example, "I may never get what I really want.")

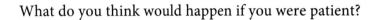

What do you think would happen if you were patient?

Do any fears underlie your impatience? Can you trace these fears to a belief?

What do you plan to do the next time these feelings arise?

CREATION STEP ONE, CONT.

FLOW-STOPPER 7: JUDGMENT

When was the last time you judged a person, situation, or thing?

What triggers judgment for you?

What benefit do you receive by judging?

Judgment often comes from a fear-based need to be "right" or "safe from wrong." What would it look like if you let go of the need to be right?

CREATION STEP ONE, CONT.

How do you think judgment energy interferes with your ability to consciously create?

What do you plan to do next time you start to judge?

CREATION STEP ONE, CONT.

{ extra writing space }

FLOW-STOPPER 8: DISAPPOINTMENT

When was the last time you felt disappointed?

What triggers disappointment for you?

What benefit do you receive by feeling disappointed?

How do you think disappointment energy interferes with your ability to consciously create?

Think about a recent disappointment. Ask yourself these questions:

Y	N	Did I give myself enough time to create what I wanted?
Y	N	Do I have a belief that says "I can't have that?"
Y	N	Do I have a belief that says, "I don't deserve that?"
Y	N	Did I let my child or adolescent self take over and push away the thing I wanted?

What is your plan for next time it happens?

Remember, it's helpful to allow yourself to really feel disappointment when it comes up – but only for a set time that YOU determine.

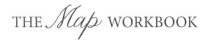

CREATION STEP ONE, CONT.

{ extra writing space }

FLOW-STOPPER 9: BLAME

When was the last time you assigned blame to someone or something?

What triggers blame for you?

What benefit do you receive by placing blame?

How do you think blaming other people, things, or situations for your reality

interferes with your power to consciously create?

What do you plan to do the next time it happens?

FLOW-STOPPER 10: ENTITLEMENT

When was the last time you felt entitled?

What triggers a sense of entitlement for you?

Do you hold any beliefs which trigger entitlement, such as "_____

owes me?"

What benefit do you receive through feeling entitled?

How do you think entitlement interferes with your power to consciously create?

What do you plan to do the next time it happens?

FLOW-STOPPER 11: GUILT

When was the last time you felt guilty?

What triggers a sense of guilt for you?

Who do you think you help by feeling guilty?

What beliefs are at the root of your guilt? Can you change them?

What do you plan to do the next time it happens?

FLOW-STOPPER 12: JEALOUSY

When was the last time you felt jealous?

What triggers jealousy for you?

What beliefs underpin your jealousy?

How do you think jealousy interferes with your power to consciously create?

What do you plan to do the next time it happens?

FLOW-STOPPER 13: SHAME

When was the last time you felt ashamed?

What triggers a sense of shame for you?

GUILT AND
SHAME ARE
NOT THE SAME,
ALTHOUGH THEY
OFTEN SHOW UP
TOGETHER. TUNE
IN TO YOUR INNER
WISDOM TO GET TO
THE CORE OF THESE
FLOW-STOPPING
ENERGIES AND TAP
INTO YOUR ABILITY
TO CREATE
100% OF YOUR
REALITY!

What has shamed you in your past? In your present?

What beliefs have you taken on from those who have shamed you?

In a meditation, give the shame back* to those who gave it to you.

How do you feel now?

· ·

* A Lazaris technique. You can find several helpful recordings for working with shame energy at Lazaris.com.

CREATION STEP *Two*

WORK WITH YOUR CHILD SELF

If you'd prefer a recorded version of this technique, visit LiveALifeYouLove.com.

Do the "Technique to Connect with Your Child Self" described on page 130 of *The Map*. Talk to your child self about how you are planning to become a conscious creator, and about any dreams you are currently working on. Let your child tell you how they feel about this. Ask them what they want/need in order to feel safe, loved, and happy—then, give it to them!

WHEN YOU'VE FINISHED THIS TECHNIQUE, ANSWER THE FOLLOWING QUESTIONS.

How does your child self feel about you creating your reality? What about your current dream? Do they have any objections? Fears? Questions?

{more writing space on the next page}

BE THOROUGH IN RECORDING YOUR CHILD'S RESPONSES. THEY MAY HIDE BELIEFS YOU DIDN'T REALIZE YOU HELD!

What did your child self want you to create for them? How did they

respond when you did it?

CREATION STEP *Three*

WORK WITH YOUR ADOLESCENT SELF

The technique to connect with your adolescent self is the same as the "Technique to Connect with Your Child Self" described on page 130 of *The Map*. Talk to your adolescent self about how you are planning to become a conscious creator, and perhaps about a current dream. Let them tell you how they feel about this. Ask them what they want/need in order to feel safe, loved, and happy—then, give it to them!

If you'd prefer a recorded version of this technique, visit LiveALifeYouLove.com.

WHEN YOU'VE FINISHED THIS TECHNIQUE, ANSWER THE FOLLOWING QUESTIONS.

How does your adolescent self feel about you creating your reality, and about the dream you shared? Do they have any objections? Fears? Questions?

{more writing space on the next page}

What did your adolescent self want you to create for them? How did they

respond when you did it?

CREATION STEP *Four*

WORK WITH YOUR YOUNG (AND OLDER) ADULT SELVES

If you'd prefer a recorded version of this technique, visit LiveALifeYouLove.com.

Do the "Technique to Connect with Your Young Adult Self" described on page 135 of *The Map*. You will be connecting with the "yous" who have experienced major disappointment, and allowing your young adult(s) to express their emotions as fully as possible. Then, you will give them what they want—whatever they didn't receive back then.

WHEN YOU'VE FINISHED THIS TECHNIQUE, ANSWER THE FOLLOWING QUESTIONS.

What disappointments did your young adult self (or selves) talk about?

{more writing space on the next page}

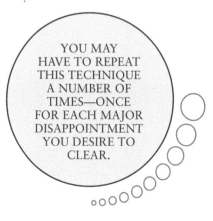

YOU MAY HAVE TO REPEAT THIS TECHNIQUE A NUMBER OF TIMES—ONCE FOR EACH MAJOR DISAPPOINTMENT YOU DESIRE TO CLEAR.

Did your young adults' emotional expression surprise you? Were they angrier or sadder than you'd thought?

How did they react when you gave them the things they desired?

CREATION STEP *Five*

WORK WITH YOUR NEGATIVE SELF

Do the "Technique to Connect with Your Negative Self" described on page 140 of *The Map*. Let your negative self know that you are becoming a masterful magician in your world. Let it rant and rave in the space below.

WHAT DOES YOUR NEGATIVE SELF HAVE TO SAY?

{more writing space on the next page}

WHEN YOUR
NEGATIVE SELF IS
FINISHED RANTING,
VISUALIZE LEAVING IT
WITH YOUR HIGHER SELF
FOR HEALING, AND TURN
THE PAGE.

→

WORKBOOK *Bonus #1*

(GENTLY) BANISH YOUR FLOW-STOPPERS

In the previous Creation Steps, you've identified your Flow-Stoppers and their triggers, and worked with your younger selves to discover how they feel about the path you're on. You've also worked with your negative self to uncover and put a stop to any negative energy it might have been flowing.

Now that you know what your Flow-Stoppers look like, here are some exercises to (gently) banish them when they rear their ugly heads.

WORKING WITH FLOW-STOPPERS

STOP VOICING YOUR NEGATIVE THOUGHTS

As we know from reading our intentions aloud, voicing a thought gives it power. Practice keeping your flow-stopping thoughts to yourself. After a while, you'll notice that they don't feel as strong or heavy. Then, work on banishing them from your mind, too!

TAKE A DEEP BREATH! Sometimes, just pausing before you react can be enough to release blocking energy.

97

FEEL THE FLOW-STOPPING ENERGY — BUT ONLY FOR A SHORT TIME OF *YOUR* CHOOSING.

Give yourself 5 to 20 minutes to truly feel your shame, jealousy, self-pity, or whatever else is coming up. Write about your feelings in your Creation Journal. Then, close the book and walk away, leaving your flow-stoppers behind on the pages.

ASK YOURSELF:

"WHAT WOULD IT FEEL LIKE *NOT* TO FEEL THIS WAY?"

By getting curious about the opposite experience, you shift the direction of your thought energy, and open to possibility. How would it feel to be patient, confident, unconditionally loving, etc.? Write about your thought explorations on your computer or in your Creation Journal.

WORK WITH YOUR BELIEFS

The belief-shifting exercises in the next chapter can help you get to the root of your Flow-Stoppers and stop them for good!

How I'm working with my flow-stoppers ...

NEED MORE WRITING SPACE? *Use your Creation Journal!*

CHAPTER SIX

THE 24/7 FLOW; BELIEFS

*"The power to move
the world is in the
subconscious mind."*

~ William James

Beliefs are thoughts and feelings that are wired into your system. These are thoughts and feelings that are so solid you take them as absolute truth. And you emit that energy, which in turn creates your reality, one hundred percent of the time.

BELIEFS
CONTROL
YOUR WORLD

When you change your beliefs you literally change your world. Your success. Your finances. Your health. Your relationships. *Everything* changes.

DISCOVERING YOUR BELIEFS

It takes some detective work to uncover the beliefs that are creating what you don't want. So where do you begin? By paying attention to:

WHAT YOU THINK
WHAT YOU FEEL
WHAT YOU SAY
WHAT YOU DO
WHAT YOU CREATE

The absolute best way of discovering your beliefs is to look at what you have already created. You may deceive yourself—or be unconscious of the truth—but your reality never lies. It reflects as clear as day what you really, deep down, truly believe.

THE THREE LEVELS OF BELIEFS

Every belief you have falls into one of these categories.

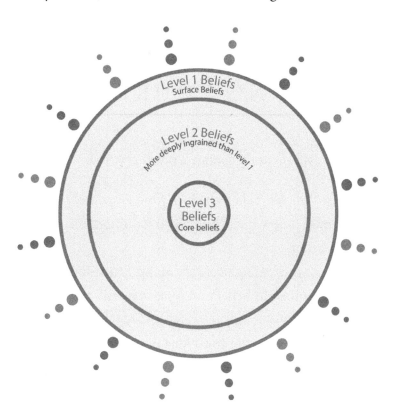

LEVEL ONE BELIEFS

Light beliefs that are not particularly old, deep, or impactful. We won't bother addressing these in this workbook, but you can read about them on page 181 of *The Map*.

LEVEL TWO BELIEFS

Deep beliefs taken from our parents, teachers, authority figures, religious leaders, media, society, and our own past experiences.

LEVEL THREE BELIEFS

Beliefs that impact every aspect of your life and creation.

There are three critical questions to ask yourself when you are seeking to uncover your beliefs:

1. What do I want to create?
2. What have I created?
3. What would someone have to believe to create this?

CHANGING YOUR BELIEFS

The basic steps to successfully change a belief are:

1. Word the old belief succinctly but accurately.
2. Choose a new belief and word it similarly to the old belief.
3. Enter the subconscious mind meditatively; destroy the old belief and replace it with the new belief.
4. Follow up with the conscious mind.

The exercises in this chapter are designed to help you uncover your beliefs, and change those that don't support your conscious reality creation. If you run out of writing space, use your Creation Journal. Don't forget to date your entries!

WORKBOOK Bonus #2

FOUNDATIONAL BELIEFS

(OR, WHERE TO BEGIN WITH BELIEF WORK)

The best place to begin with belief work is to look at your foundational beliefs. If I've heard it once, I've heard it a dozen times: "But Boni, I followed everything in the book, and it just isn't working!"

"It *always* works," I counter.

Still, it hadn't worked for them, and it may not be working for you. As with everything, everywhere, everywhen, there's always a reason why it isn't working.

Of course, I can't really tell why your particular dream hasn't manifested. It may be that you are stuck in a flow-stopper like self-pity or martyr energy. It may be that you stopped flowing positive energy towards your desire and you only pay attention to what you don't have (yep, that would mean you're creating *not getting* your dream).

But sometimes, you're doing everything right, and your dream still hasn't manifested—not even a sign.

The likely culprit …

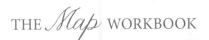

YOUR FOUNDATIONAL BELIEFS

Foundational beliefs are beliefs about beliefs themselves, about creating reality, and about your ability to create your reality and/or change your beliefs.

Foundational beliefs will sabotage your belief-changing work, and ultimately your entire dream. Foundational beliefs are beliefs such as:

It is impossible to create my own reality.

If you hold that belief, no matter how many books you read or how much work you do to create your world, that belief will make it impossible!

FOUNDATIONAL BELIEFS MUST BE CHANGED BEFORE ANY OTHER BELIEFS IN ORDER TO SUCCESSFULLY AND EASILY MOVE FORWARD.

To help you identify any foundational beliefs you may hold, I have broken down these "mothers of all beliefs" into categories to make them easier to identify.

If any of these beliefs sound familiar to you, check the box next to the belief, so you can refer to it when you begin your belief-changing exercises later in this section.

IT IS NOT POSSIBLE/EASY

- [ ] *We don't really create our own realities.*
- [ ] *I cannot create my reality.*
- [ ] *I cannot change my beliefs.*
- [ ] *It is difficult to create my reality.*
- [ ] *It is hard to change beliefs.*
- [ ] *I cannot easily discover my subconscious beliefs.*
- [ ] *I cannot change my beliefs about _____ (money, love, men, women, health, work, other people, etc.).*

IT WORKS FOR EVERYONE ELSE BUT ME

- [ ] *Even if I change my beliefs, my world will not change.*
- [ ] *Nothing ever works for me.*
- [ ] *I do not have what it takes to change my beliefs and my life.*
- [ ] *I do not have the power or ability to create my world.*
- [ ] *It is hard to create what I want.*
- [ ] *I am not powerful enough to change my beliefs.*

IT IS WRONG/UNSPIRITUAL TO CREATE MY REALITY

- [ ] *It is wrong to change my beliefs.*
- [ ] *I will be punished if I change my beliefs.*
- [ ] *Only God can change my beliefs.*
- [ ] *It is unspiritual to change my beliefs.*
- [ ] *Only God can create my reality.*
- [ ] *It is blasphemous to believe I can create my own reality.*

I'M NOT READY

- ☐ *I am not ready to change my beliefs about _____ (money, love, men, health, work, other people, etc.).*

- ☐ *I am not ready for the success that will happen when I change my beliefs.*

- ☐ *I can have the realities I desire after I clear out all my blockages.*

- ☐ *I am not healed enough to create my reality.*

- ☐ *If I successfully create my own reality the responsibility of that would be too much for me to handle.*

- ☐ *I am not _____ (old, young, wise, capable, seasoned, experienced, smart, etc.) enough to create my own reality.*

IT'S NOT SAFE:

- ☐ *The success that happens as a result of changing my beliefs will make people I care about feel badly about their own lives.*

- ☐ *If I change my beliefs about _____ (money, love, men, health, work, other people, etc.) and my world changes, someone I care about (use an actual name) will be hurt.*

- ☐ *Something bad will happen if I change my beliefs.*

- ☐ *It is not safe to create all that I want.*

- ☐ *If I believe in this information others will ridicule me.*

Can you understand how debilitating these beliefs are? How they can stop you from moving forward before you even get started?

The most important work you will ever do in conscious creation is changing your beliefs. Nothing will shift you forward faster when you do it. Nothing will hold you back longer if you don't.

To determine whether you are holding any foundational beliefs, I suggest using the applied kinesiology method (outlined in Workbook Bonus 4 on page 167) in conjunction with other methods of determining beliefs (covered in more detail in *The Map*), including:

1. Asking yourself if your reality reflects the belief.

2. Asking yourself whether it feels accurate to you in your gut.

3. Asking your child, adolescent, and young adult selves about their beliefs on creating your reality and changing beliefs.

{ Writing Space }

CREATION STEP *One*

RELEASE NEGATIVE FEELINGS AND EMOTIONAL BAGGAGE

If you still feel angry, betrayed, hurt, abandoned, mistreated, etc. by something or someone in your past, it *will* stop you from moving forward in the future. One great way to release these emotions is to write a "hate letter" to yourself, another person, or even God. As you write, release your negative feelings onto the page.

MY HATE LETTER

Dear _____ ,

WHEN YOU'VE FINISHED WRITING, TEAR OUT THIS PAGE AND BURN IT IN A SAFE PLACE (LIKE OVER THE KITCHEN SINK). AS IT BURNS TO ASH, RELEASE ANY NEGATIVE FEELINGS AND SAY ALOUD, "I FORGIVE YOU. I FORGIVE MYSELF."

CREATION STEP *Two*

WHAT YOU *THINK* IS A CLUE ABOUT YOUR BELIEFS

Spend some time noticing your thoughts as they arise—especially those that pertain to the thing you want to create. How do you think about yourself (in relation to your desired creation)?

Write down all of your thoughts, both positive and negative.

POSITIVE THOUGHTS

NEGATIVE THOUGHTS

Over the course of your observation, did you notice that you have more

positive thoughts, or more negative ones? Why do you think that is?

THOUGHTS = BELIEFS

Now, from the thoughts you recorded, create two lists of the beliefs those thoughts represent: one for the positive beliefs you want to reinforce, and one for the negative beliefs you want to change. Remember, you can (and do) have conflicting beliefs—two absolutely opposite beliefs—and *you can believe them both at the same time*!

BELIEFS TO KEEP

BELIEFS TO CHANGE

YOU'LL WORK
WITH THIS SECOND
SET OF BELIEFS LATER
IN THIS CHAPTER. FOR
NOW, SET THEM ASIDE,
AND MOVE ON TO THE
NEXT PAGE.

→

CREATION STEP *Three*

WHAT YOU *FEEL* IS A CLUE ABOUT YOUR BELIEFS

Spend some time noticing your emotions as you think about your dreams coming true. What makes you fearful? What makes you anxious? What makes you jump for joy?

Be conscious of your emotions throughout the day. Do they fluctuate? Do you anger easily, become impatient, or feel overwhelmed? What is your pattern of emotions on a typical day? These are creating your future!

HOW I FEEL
(about my conscious reality creation, intentions, and day-to-day life)

Now, create a list of feelings you want to encourage, and another of feelings you want to change.

FEELINGS TO ENCOURAGE

FEELINGS TO CHANGE

CREATION STEP THREE, CONT.

FEELINGS = BELIEFS

Create a list of beliefs you want to change from your list of feelings on the previous page. You'll work with this list again later in this chapter.

FEELING

BELIEF

_____   _____

_____   _____

_____   _____

_____   _____

_____   _____

_____   _____

_____   _____

_____   _____

_____   _____

_____   _____

{ extra writing space }

CREATION STEP *Four*

WHAT YOU *SAY* IS A CLUE ABOUT YOUR BELIEFS

Words reveal your beliefs—sometimes before you're even aware of what you've said! Notice if there are words, phrases, idioms, or clichés you use all the time. If you can, ask someone close to you to point out your self-loving and self-sabotaging phrases. Write these down. (There's extra writing space on the next page, too.)

WHAT I SAY

(about myself, my reality, my dreams, and others)

{ extra writing space }

CREATION STEP FOUR, CONT.

WORDS & PHRASES = BELIEFS

From your list of "most popular" words and phrases, create two lists of the beliefs they represent: one of the beliefs you want to keep, and another of beliefs you want to change.

BELIEFS TO KEEP

BELIEFS TO CHANGE

{ extra writing space }

CREATION STEP *Five*

WHAT YOU *DO* IS A CLUE ABOUT YOUR BELIEFS

Your actions are a clue to your beliefs, just like your thoughts, words, and feelings. Take some time to notice where your desires and your actions aren't lining up. This will tell you a lot about what you believe about your dreams, goals, and intentions.

WHAT I WANT TO DO

_____

_____

_____

_____

_____

_____

_____

_____

_____

_____

_____

WHAT I DO

_____

_____

_____

_____

_____

_____

_____

_____

_____

_____

_____

ACTIONS = BELIEFS

When was the last time you took action to create something you said you wanted, or to change something you said you wanted to change?

What tasks or actions do you keep putting off, or make excuses for not doing?

CREATION STEP FIVE, CONT.

What do your actions tell you about your beliefs?

BELIEFS TO CHANGE

(You'll work with this list later in this chapter.)

IF YOU'RE NOT SURE WHAT YOUR ACTIONS SAY ABOUT YOUR BELIEFS, ASK YOURSELF: "WHAT WOULD SOMEONE HAVE TO BELIEVE TO DO _____ WHEN THEY SAY THEY WANT _____?"

More info on uncovering beliefs can be found in Chapter Six of *The Map*.

CREATION STEP FIVE, CONT.

{ extra writing space }

CREATION STEP *Six*

WHAT *OTHERS CREATE* IS A CLUE ABOUT YOUR BELIEFS

Your beliefs show up in the lives of others. What are you creating in the world around you? In the lives of your friends and family? In your community? In society at large? What do you see everywhere you look?

OTHERS' CREATIONS = MY BELIEFS

Look at the people in your life who inspire jealousy, pity, or judgment. What do your feelings about them reveal about your own beliefs?

CREATION STEP SIX, CONT.

BELIEFS TO CHANGE

(You'll work with this list later in this chapter.)

CREATION STEP *Seven*

WHAT *YOU CREATE* IS THE BEST AND BIGGEST CLUE
ABOUT YOUR BELIEFS

Where does your reality differ from what you want to create?

WHAT I HAVE

_____

_____

_____

_____

_____

_____

_____

_____

_____

_____

_____

WHAT I WANT

_____

_____

_____

_____

_____

_____

_____

_____

_____

_____

_____

MY REALITY = MY BELIEFS

Look at the disparities between your current reality and what you want to create. What do these gaps tell you about your beliefs? Ask yourself, "What would someone have to believe in order to create what I've created?"

On the next page, write out each belief you uncover. Use the techniques in Chapter Six to change these beliefs.

BELIEF 1

BELIEF 2

BELIEF 3

BELIEF 4

 BELIEF 5

 BELIEF 6

 BELIEF 7

 BELIEF 8

CREATION STEP *Eight*

WHAT DO YOUR YOUNGER SELVES BELIEVE?

Revisit your work with your child, adolescent, and young adult selves in the previous chapter. What beliefs did you uncover about yourself, your world, and your ability to consciously create what you desire?

Beliefs I discovered through my child:

Beliefs I discovered through my adolescent:

 Beliefs I discovered through my young adult(s):

CREATION STEP *Nine*

CONSCIOUS & UNCONSCIOUS BELIEFS

Now, review the beliefs you compiled during the exercises earlier in this chapter. You'll probably notice that there are similar themes running throughout.

You may have also noticed that some of your beliefs are in conflict with one another. This is because there is a difference between beliefs we hold *consciously* (the ones we choose to believe) and the beliefs we hold *unconsciously* (the ones we don't know or don't want to admit we have).

CONSCIOUS	UNCONSCIOUS
The Universe/God is loving	The Universe/God is judgmental
I am good enough	I am not good enough
I am unconditionally loved	I am not loved/lovable
I can create my reality	I cannot create my reality

As you can see, it's possible for your unconscious beliefs to be exactly opposite to your conscious beliefs!

SIT WITH THE FOLLOWING QUESTIONS:

Are any of the beliefs you discovered when working with your younger selves opposed to the beliefs you hold consciously?

Are there any beliefs you don't want to admit to holding? How can you lovingly accept and change these?

NEED MORE WRITING SPACE? *Use your Creation Journal!*

In the next Creation Step, you'll take the first steps toward changing your unconscious beliefs.

CREATION STEP

CHANGE YOUR BELIEFS, CHANGE YOUR WORLD

The overall components to successfully change a belief are:

- Word the old belief succinctly but accurately.

- Choose a new belief and word it similarly to the old belief.

- Enter the subconscious mind in meditation, destroy the old belief, and replace it with the new one.

- Follow up with the conscious mind.

WORDING IS KEY

Your beliefs will be easily substituted in your subconscious mind if you've worded them properly and succinctly.

A belief might be accurate but still be too wordy for your subconscious mind to change with ease. Here's an example:

If I find something fun, I won't be able to be successful with it and make money with it, too.

If you can, shorten the belief without losing the substance of it.

I can't have money, fun, and success all at the same time.

The most important thing is that the belief feels true to you. And please, don't let the technicality of the wording stop you from changing your beliefs. They don't have to be perfect—but they do need to feel accurate.

CONSOLIDATE BELIEFS WHERE APPROPRIATE

In the work you've done so far to discover your beliefs, you may have found that you have duplicate beliefs. It is fine to consolidate these into a single belief to change, as long as all of the duplicates feel like they mean *exactly* the same thing.

For example, maybe you discovered a belief through your child that says,

I'm so stupid, I can't do anything.

And, when you looked at what you create, you found a belief that says,

When I try something, I inevitably fail because I miss something or I just don't have what it takes.

The critical piece is that, when you consolidate two (or more) beliefs, they must mean exactly the same thing to you, and feel the same when you say them. In this case, the belief might be:

I am not smart enough to create my dreams.

If, however, the beliefs are not exactly the same—or even if they look the same but don't *feel* the same when you say them—it's best to treat them as separate.

MASTER LIST OF
BELIEFS TO CHANGE

It's time to gather all of the beliefs you uncovered during your work with the previous Creation Steps in this chapter. Word each belief accurately and succinctly, combining any beliefs that are identical. Then, write the new belief below the old one, keeping the wording as similar as possible to make it easier for your subconscious to absorb.

OLD BELIEF 1:

NEW BELIEF 1:

OLD BELIEF 2:

NEW BELIEF 2:

🌱 **OLD BELIEF 3:**

NEW BELIEF 3:

🌱 **OLD BELIEF 4:**

NEW BELIEF 4:

🌱 **OLD BELIEF 5:**

NEW BELIEF 5:

🌱 **OLD BELIEF 6:**

NEW BELIEF 6:

CREATION STEP TEN, CONT.

❧ OLD BELIEF 7:

NEW BELIEF 7:

❧ OLD BELIEF 8:

NEW BELIEF 8:

❧ OLD BELIEF 9:

NEW BELIEF 9:

❧ OLD BELIEF 10:

NEW BELIEF 10:

REMEMBER TO
WORD THE NEW
BELIEF AS SIMILARLY
AS POSSIBLE TO THE
OLD ONE.

OLD BELIEF 11:

NEW BELIEF 11:

OLD BELIEF 12:

NEW BELIEF 12:

OLD BELIEF 13:

NEW BELIEF 13:

OLD BELIEF 14:

NEW BELIEF 14:

CREATION STEP TEN, CONT.

     OLD BELIEF 15:

     NEW BELIEF 15:

     OLD BELIEF 16:

     NEW BELIEF 16:

     OLD BELIEF 17:

     NEW BELIEF 17:

     OLD BELIEF 18:

     NEW BELIEF 18:

❧ **OLD BELIEF 19:**

NEW BELIEF 19:

❧ **OLD BELIEF 20:**

NEW BELIEF 20:

❧ **OLD BELIEF 21:**

NEW BELIEF 21:

❧ **OLD BELIEF 22:**

NEW BELIEF 22:

CREATION STEP TEN, CONT.

🌱 **OLD BELIEF 23:**

NEW BELIEF 23:

🌱 **OLD BELIEF 24:**

NEW BELIEF 24:

🌱 **OLD BELIEF 25:**

NEW BELIEF 25:

🌱 **OLD BELIEF 26:**

NEW BELIEF 26:

OLD BELIEF 27:

NEW BELIEF 27:

 OLD BELIEF 28:

NEW BELIEF 28:

 OLD BELIEF 29:

NEW BELIEF 29:

 OLD BELIEF 30:

NEW BELIEF 30:

CHANGE YOUR BELIEFS IN YOUR SUBCONSCIOUS MIND

MEDITATION TO CHANGE YOUR LEVEL TWO BELIEFS

Have your master list of old and new beliefs handy. Get into a quiet space, and close your eyes. Call upon your unseen friends to assist you.

Imagine yourself in a beautiful place in nature. This place is serene, quiet, and safe. Imagine your unseen friends coming to be with you, surrounding you in a bubble of love and light. Take a moment to close your mental eyes and feel the wonderful love and light. Feel the love, guidance, and protection of your unseen friends.

When you open your mental eyes, you are surrounded by mist. Before you is a grand marble staircase. You and your unseen friends walk up this staircase … up, up, up into the clouds.

At the very top of the staircase, you will see the entrance to a city, which represents your subconscious mind. This city may be modern, or ancient. It could be a city of nature. It could change shape. Whatever it looks like, though, is perfect for you.

The king or queen of this city (your subconscious) will soon come to welcome you. Tell them that you want to change your beliefs. They will look to your higher self for permission, and your higher self will nod their consent.

Follow the king/queen to the Building of Beliefs. Your higher self will join you.

The king/queen takes you to the room in this building that holds your Level Two beliefs. This is a gigantic, circular room, lined floor to ceiling with filing cabinets. There is a ladder that slides around the room on a rail, to access the high drawers. You gaze around in amazement.

Tell the king/queen the first belief you want to change. (It's okay to peek at your paper.) The king/queen will go to a drawer, and pull out a paper. There is your belief, written on a piece of card stock, plain as day!

Take the belief to the small table in the center of the room. On the table is a big, fat, black marker. Take off the cap, and cross out the old belief. Be sure to strike through every word! Then, rip the old belief into tiny pieces, and place it in the silver bowl which is lying on the tabletop. Your higher self points a finger, and the paper bursts into flame, quickly extinguishing and leaving nothing—not even ashes—behind.

Take a clean, white piece of card stock from the shelf under the table, and with a smaller black marker, write out your new belief. Feel your hand shape each letter and say each word in your mind as you write it.

Hand the new belief to the king/queen and ask them to re-file it.

Repeat this process with every belief you want to change. When you're finished, thank your higher self and the king/queen. They will appreciatively accept your thanks.

When you're ready, open your eyes.

If you'd like to purchase a guided meditation for changing your beliefs, visit LiveALifeYouLove.com

150

CONSCIOUS MIND FOLLOW-UP

Write out your new Level Two beliefs in the space below. Read them aloud, today and every day for sixty days, with as much excitement as you can muster.

MY NEW LEVEL TWO BELIEFS

THE *Map* WORKBOOK

{ extra writing space }

CREATION STEP TEN, CONT.

How does it feel to hold these new beliefs?

Write about your experience with changing your beliefs in the space below. Which beliefs were hard to change? Which were easy? How did you feel about the overall process?

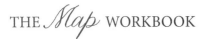

{ extra writing space }

CREATION STEP *Eleven*

CORE (LEVEL THREE) BELIEFS

Level Three beliefs are the primary reason we hit a plateau in our creating. Therefore, it's important to take the time to change these beliefs, no matter how challenging the process may seem.

Generally, we all have one, or maybe two, core beliefs. (Unlike Level Two beliefs, of which we have loads!) Our core beliefs are the most critical ones to change. They are harder to uncover than Level Two beliefs, but once you've changed them, the results show up everywhere!

COMMON CORE BELIEFS

Do you hold any of these core beliefs?

I DON'T DESERVE.

I AM NOT GOOD ENOUGH.

I DON'T MATTER.

I AM NOT WORTHY.

I AM FLAWED.

I'M NOT ENOUGH.

How do you discover if you have a Level Three belief? The same way you discovered your Level Two beliefs! You can also use the Applied Kinesiology practice outlined in Workbook Bonus #4, or the technique outlined in Workbook Bonus #3 on the next page.

WORKBOOK *Bonus # 3*

DRILLING DOWN TO A CORE BELIEF

It can be difficult to own up to the fact that you have a core belief such as, "I'm not good enough." I know it was for me. But I'm willing to bet that, unless your life is working sublimely in every way, you have an unhelpful core belief, too.

How does one discover a core belief? There are many ways to go about it (including the tools provided in Chapter Six of *The Map*), but here's one that might help you to be certain. *NOTE: Extreme emotional honesty is required for this exercise.*

WHAT IS YOUR GREATEST FEAR?

This is the fear that keeps you up at night, the fear that is underneath all other fears. This is the fear you don't admit to others—the fear that you're reluctant to even admit to yourself. Here's an example: "*I fear that I'll die before I really get to live my dream.*"

Write out your greatest fear below.

WHY MIGHT THIS HAPPEN? Example: *"Because I just don't have what it takes to create it."* Again, extreme honesty is the key here.

WHY? Example: *"Because no matter how hard I try, I just can't seem to pull off the big ones."*

AGAIN, WHY? Example: *"I'm not sure. I just don't think I'm ... enough."*

WHAT'S UNDERNEATH THAT? Examples: *"Nothing. I'm just not enough."* Or, *"I'm not good enough."* Or, *"I'm not important enough."*

You'll know when you've drilled down enough because there won't be anything else. It will be the last thing you know to be true about this fear. And it will hit you in the gut. It might be emotional. And you'll just know it is true.

THIS IS YOUR CORE (LEVEL THREE) BELIEF. AND NOW THAT YOU'VE IDENTIFIED IT, YOU CAN USE THE TOOLS IN THIS SECTION TO CHANGE IT!

{ Writing Space }

CREATION STEP ELEVEN, CONT.

CHANGING YOUR CORE BELIEF

Changing a core belief requires a little more work than changing Level Two beliefs. This work begins with contemplation and answering the questions below.

The more thoroughly and honestly you answer these questions, the more likely you are to be successful in changing your belief.

CORE BELIEF: _____

How has this belief affected you for your entire life?

Why DON'T you want to change this belief?

Need to review this technique? Go to page 130 of *The Map*.

What does your child self need to be okay with changing this belief? How can you give it to them?

What does your adolescent self need to be okay with changing this belief? How can you give it to them?

What do your young adult selves need to be okay with changing this belief? How can you give it to them?

MY NEW BELIEF: _____

How will your life change with this new core belief?

How will your self-concept shift when you change this belief?

Use the Level Three Belief-Changing technique on the next page to change this belief. Write about the process in a document on your computer or in your Creation Journal.

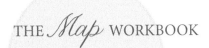

CHANGE YOUR LEVEL THREE (CORE) BELIEF IN YOUR SUBCONSCIOUS MIND

Have your old and new Level Three belief(s) handy. Get into a quiet space, and close your eyes. Call upon your unseen friends to assist you.

Imagine yourself in a beautiful place in nature. This place is serene, quiet, and safe. Imagine your unseen friends coming to be with you, surrounding you in a bubble of love and light. Take a moment to close your mental eyes and feel the wonderful love and light. Feel the love, guidance, and protection of your unseen friends.

When you open your mental eyes, you are surrounded by mist. Before you is a grand marble staircase. You and your unseen friends walk up this staircase … up, up, up into the clouds.

At the very top of the staircase, you will see the entrance to a city, which represents your subconscious mind. This city may be modern, or ancient. It could be a city of nature. It could change shape. Whatever it looks like, though, is perfect for you.

Do a separate meditation for each Level Three belief you want to change. This ensures that each change is powerful!

The king or queen of this city (your subconscious) will soon come to welcome you. Tell them that you want to change your beliefs. They will look to your higher self for permission, and your higher self will nod their consent. "Are you *sure*?" they will ask.

Your higher self will look at you, and then back at the king/queen, and say, "Yes. It is time."

Follow the king/queen to the Building of Beliefs. Your higher self will join you.

The king/queen takes you to the room in this building that holds your Level Three beliefs. They press a secret button (you can't tell exactly how) and an entire section of cabinets opens up to reveal a secret door.

The king/queen goes through the doorway and beckons you to follow. You and your higher self do follow, but you barely catch a glimpse of the king/queen as they head down a hallway and around a corner. They twist through long passages, this way and that. Finally, they enter an elevator. You follow, barely making it inside before the doors close.

The elevator goes up, over, down, over, up … again and again. You lose track entirely of where you are. Finally, the doors open, and the king/queen leads you to a door marked "Core Beliefs: Do Not Enter."

The king/queen unlocks the door and allows you to enter. It's a small room with a table in the middle. On the table is a thin book marked, "Core Beliefs."

"Now," the king/queen says, "Tell me the belief you want to change."

Tell them, using crystal clear wording. They will open the book to that belief.

Pick up your thick, black marker. Cross out the old belief, obliterating every word. Then, rip the page completely out of the book, and tear it to tiny shreds.

Your higher self will look at you and ask, "Are you certain? This will change everything!" Nod your head. You are ready to change this belief. Your higher self points a finger, and the paper bursts into flame, quickly extinguishing and leaving nothing—not even ashes—behind.

Look down at the book. There is a clean, white page where your old belief used to be. With a smaller black marker, write out your new belief on this page. Feel your hand shape each letter and say each word in your mind as you write it. When you're done, put down the marker and close the book.

Your higher self and the king/queen are grinning. Grin back, thanking them with your eyes. Then, say your good-byes, and allow yourself to be back where you started … but you're different now.

CONSCIOUS MIND FOLLOW-UP

Write out your new Level Three belief in the space below. (If you changed more than one belief, create a new page for each one on your computer or in your Creation Journal.) Read your new belief aloud, today and every day for ninety days, with as much excitement as you can muster.

If you'd like to purchase a guided meditation for changing your beliefs, visit LiveALifeYouLove.com

MY NEW LEVEL THREE BELIEF:

How does it feel to hold this new belief?

Write about your experience with changing your Level Three belief in the space below. How did you feel about the overall process?

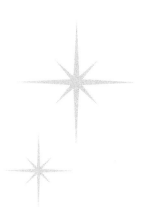

CREATION STEP ELEVEN, CONT.

{ extra writing space }

WORKBOOK *Bonus #4*

LET YOUR BODY TELL YOU IF YOU HAVE A BELIEF

You may be asking, "How do I tell if a belief is mine?" I have asked that question myself, and for a long time my only answers were, "If it is reflected in your world, it is yours," or, "Use your gut to determine if it's yours."

NOTE: THIS TECHNIQUE DOES NOT INDICATE WHETHER SOMETHING IS TRUE OR FALSE FOR OTHERS OR IN THE WORLD— ONLY WHETHER IT IS PREDOMINANTLY TRUE OR FALSE IN YOUR SUBCONSCIOUS MIND.

But sometimes it isn't that easy to tell. So I teach a form of applied kinesiology that can help you determine whether you hold a belief.

Applied kinesiology (also called "muscle testing") allows the body to indicate a true or false response when presented with a statement. The reason that applied kinesiology works is that the body is essentially an electrical circuit. Energy is always flowing within that circuitry.

When your energy is flowing smoothly, your body works the way it is supposed to. When something blocks the energy from flowing, your body doesn't work as well. In this case, it becomes wobbly and your muscles don't hold strong.

THIS TEST MAY NOT WORK FOR EVERYONE. Why? Because some people really want to control and don't feel safe letting their bodies take over for a bit. If it isn't working for you (after you've changed your beliefs about applied kinesiology), use one or more other methods of determining beliefs covered in more detail in *The Map*.

What causes the blockage? Anything that is untrue will cause an energy blockage. This is how we can use applied kinesiology to indicate whether we believe something or not.

169

This method works very well if you are centered and calm and believe it will work. If you suspect you might not let this work, before anything, change these beliefs:

Applied kinesiology will not work for me to determine my beliefs. It is not safe to use applied kinesiology to determine my beliefs.

Once you've changed those beliefs, you are ready to test!

TEST YOUR BELIEFS WITH APPLIED KINESIOLOGY

- Do your testing in a quiet place where you will not be disturbed. Turn off your phone and other devices.

- Remove your shoes.

- Become calm and centered. Take a few deep breaths to increase your centeredness.

- Stand up straight, with your feet shoulder width apart.

- Clear your energy field by tapping lightly on your thymus (that little bump on your chest just under your throat), throat, and forehead.

- First practice how the true/untrue answers show themselves in your body. Close your eyes and say, "My name is (say your name)."

- Notice that your body remains solid and strong. It will not be difficult to stand without swaying.

- Next, with your eyes still closed, say, "My name is (and make up a name or say someone else's name)." You will notice your body will either fall back, fall forward, or otherwise become wobbly. It does this because the "untruth" of saying the name that isn't yours interferes with the energy flow of your body, causing your body to sway.

- Repeat this "name game" a few times until you feel good about telling the difference between true and untrue in your body.

- Now say the belief you suspect you hold, such as "I create my own reality." If you do hold that belief, your body will hold strong and solid. If you do not hold the belief, your body will falter. Basically: strong = yes, wobbly = no.

ADDITIONAL INFORMATION

I have found it's best to test a few beliefs at a time with this method, then rest for a while and test a few more. That way, you don't get confused by the signals your body is sending.

Also, remember you can easily hold two opposing beliefs at the same time, and while your conscious mind may believe something, if you hold the opposite belief in your subconscious mind, it will show up in your testing.

Often, we don't realize which beliefs we hold subconsciously because our conscious minds hold (and want to hold) the opposite beliefs. This is why this test is so useful. This is also why it is a good idea to test the negative beliefs rather than the positive ones.

{ Writing Space }

REINFORCING WITH EXAMPLES

Once you've changed your beliefs, following up with the conscious mind is critical. Reading your beliefs (with positive emotion) is a must. Beyond that reinforcement, another way to buoy your spirits and strengthen the new belief(s) is to find and acknowledge examples of the new belief in your world.

Luckily, we live in an age with plentiful information. Use Google for this exercise, and also include any examples you have in your real-life world For instance, if your new belief is: *"I can create a successful, rewarding and monetarily abundant online business while being a good mother to my two preschool children,"* you might search Google for "successful mom-preneurs."

BELIEF REINFORCEMENT

Write a new belief (choose one of the more challenging ones) below.

Research examples of your new belief. Write three of them below. Then, start a file on your computer or in your Creation Journal with additional articles and examples.

Revisit the "belief reinforcement file" weekly, if not more often, during the sixty or ninety days you are reinforcing the new belief. Spend 10-15 minutes reading over the file, doing more research, and adding to it.

How has this exercise improved the "believability" of your new belief?

CHAPTER SEVEN

TECHNIQUES TO INCREASE THE FLOW

"Travelers, there is no path. Paths are made by walking."

- Antonio Machada

Techniques can help you make things happen in the world of conscious creation. They focus the flow of energy in a laser-like way and speed the manifestation process *way* up.

There are neither good nor bad techniques, only effective or ineffective techniques for you.

One of the most important things to remember when using techniques to increase the flow is that, at some point, you have to *let go* and trust the Universe to handle the details of your manifestation. Although this may always present somewhat of a challenge, it will get easier.

CREATION STEP *One*

LEARNING FROM THE PAST

Pick an area of your life that you would like to see change (career, money, relationships, etc.). Write about your past in that area, listing the major happenings (jobs, financial history, partners, etc.), what was good about each, and what you learned.

My past experiences:

Now, let the past go with love. Imagine that the words you just wrote symbolize all of the energy, good and bad, from those past experiences. Then imagine the words floating away, along with all the emotion tied to that past. Feel gratitude for those past experiences and what you learned.

You are now free to create a new future. Write a few sentences about how this feels.

CREATION STEP *Two*

IGNITING INTENTIONS TECHNIQUE

You wrote out your intentions in Chapter Four of this workbook. Now, we'll revisit them and light them on fire (metaphorically, that is)!

This technique is a way to put attention on and flow energy to your whole list of intentions, from your Overall Intention to your Immediate Intentions.

The technique is simple. Every morning and evening for the next fourteen days, read your intentions aloud. Don't make excuses, just do it. Use the checklist below to help keep yourself accountable.

DAY 1	DAY 2	DAY 3	DAY 4	DAY 5	DAY 6	DAY 7
AM ____	AM ____	AM ____	AM ____	AM ____	AM ____	AM ____
PM ____	PM ____	PM ____	PM ____	PM ____	PM ____	PM ____
DAY 8	DAY 9	DAY 10	DAY 11	DAY 12	DAY 13	DAY 14
AM ____	AM ____	AM ____	AM ____	AM ____	AM ____	AM ____
PM ____	PM ____	PM ____	PM ____	PM ____	PM ____	PM ____

Write about your experience with the "Igniting Intentions" technique in the space below. Were you resistant? Excited? Inspired?

LIKE THIS TECHNIQUE?
You don't have to stop after 14 days! The more you use "Igniting Intentions," the better it works!

CREATION STEP *Three*

"A DAY IN THE DAY OF THE DREAM" TECHNIQUE

This is a technique to help you live (emotionally) a day in the life of the person you are becoming. Basically, you'll pretend that you already are that person! (This does not mean maxing out your credit cards because you want to become a millionaire. It does mean *feeling* as though you have all the money in the world.)

USE THE PROMPTS BELOW TO HELP YOU CREATE YOUR "DAY IN THE DAY OF THE DREAM."

You've just woken up into your dream. How do you feel? What does your morning routine look like? Who is there with you?

THIS TECHNIQUE TAKES SOME SERIOUS IMAGINATION—but let me warn you, once you start this technique, it may become addictive. And, if you do it correctly, it will eventually seem that the person you're imagining *is* you; after that, it won't be long before your responsive Universe delivers the manifestations that you have created in your "feels-oh-so-real" playacting.

How will your daily work, chores, errands, and routines look and feel different now that you are living your dream?

What new things and people will be present in your life?

What new emotions?

CREATION STEP THREE, CONT.

What new personas (celebrity, millionaire, entrepreneur, pro athlete, happily married person, new parent, etc.) do you want to try on?

If you were that dream person, how would you react to common life situations? How would you move through your world?

NOW, IT'S TIME TO ACTUALLY LIVE YOUR DREAM FOR A DAY!

When the day is over, write about your experience here.

Need more info
on this technique?
Go to page 205 of
The Map.

CREATION STEP *Four*

"MAKE THE MOVIE REAL" TECHNIQUE

What will your dream life look like in five years? Write about it here.

DO THE "MAKE THE MOVIE REAL" TECHNIQUE:

Close your eyes and imagine walking up to a move theater—the old-fashioned kind with a marquee outside and a stage within. On the marquee, you see your name in lights! The announcement reads, "_____'s Life in Five Years!"

Intrigued, you head into the theater. It's empty, and you sit in the front row. The lights dim, the curtain opens, and the movie begins.

If you'd prefer a recorded version of this technique, visit LiveALifeYouLove.com.

You see yourself—the "you" you want to become, who lives the life you desire—on the screen. Maybe you're witnessing an

average day in your life five years from now, or maybe you're seeing a special day—the day you receive an award, get married, move into a new house, go on a dream vacation, etc.

You watch this "you" for a while. At some point, the movie starts to look so real, so three-dimensional, that you can't resist climbing onto the stage and through the screen, into that life.

Up close, you observe this new you. Because you're having so much fun, you step into this future body—and suddenly, you *are* the future you!

Hang out in this future life for a while. Have fun with it. Feel the emotions that the future you experiences. Then, when you're ready, close your mental eyes and feel yourself back in the here and now.

You'll feel a little different. Embrace the change!

NOW, ANSWER THE QUESTIONS BELOW.

How did the experience of your movie feel?

Did any of the images you saw surprise you?

Were you easily able to climb into the movie and merge with your future self?

CREATION STEP *Five*

"GRATEFUL FOR NOW AND THEN" TECHNIQUE

What ten things are you are grateful for today?

TODAY'S DATE _____

❧ *I am grateful for ...*

❧ *I am grateful for ...*

❧ *I am grateful for ...*

❧ *I am grateful for ...*

❧ *I am grateful for ...*

❧ *I am grateful for ...*

❧ *I am grateful for ...*

❧ *I am grateful for ...*

❧ *I am grateful for ...*

❧ *I am grateful for ...*

What ten things are you will be grateful for at some point in the future?

FUTURE DATE _____

🌱 *I am grateful for ...*

 🌱 *I am grateful for ...*

  🌱 *I am grateful for ...*

   🌱 *I am grateful for ...*

   🌱 *I am grateful for ...*

   🌱 *I am grateful for ...*

   🌱 *I am grateful for ...*

  🌱 *I am grateful for ...*

 🌱 *I am grateful for ...*

🌱 *I am grateful for ...*

DON'T GO TOO FAR INTO THE FUTURE WITH THIS TECHNIQUE. A week, a month, or a year are great points to choose. (For more, see page 210 of *The Map*.)

CREATION STEP  *Six*

FLOW AND LET GO

The following reflections are designed to help you understand which techniques work best for you, so you can keep increasing your flow and manifesting your desires.

* * * * * *

Which of the techniques you tried were fun and creative for you?

Which felt like work or struggle?

Are there any aspects of your conscious creation that you are struggling to control or hang on to?

What would it feel like to trust that the steps you have already taken toward creation are enough for right now?

CREATION STEP SIX, CONT.

What does your inner knowing tell you about your process?

How can you shift your thoughts, words, beliefs, and actions to tell the Universe, "I already have my dream?"

CHAPTER EIGHT

ACTION: ACCELERATING THE PROCESS

Action is a proving ground for your intentions.

When you have clarified your desire and given that desire energy, taking action should feel positive. If it doesn't, you need to go back and understand why. If taking action doesn't feel good, or you aren't motivated to take action, something is wrong and needs tending to.

Action intensifies the energies and speeds up the manifestation. If you felt joyous about what you wanted and believed you could have it, you would want to get out there and begin doing it, preparing for it, taking steps towards it, etc. Those actions create more positive energy, which allows your reality to shift, creating what you want even sooner!

Action should be part of the fun. The old adage, "It's not about the destination; it's about the journey" is a critically important concept in manifesting your dreams. It's the energy of fun, excitement, and fulfillment you feel along the way that draws to you the reality you desire. You know you are on the right path when the journey towards your dreams is a blast!

Although techniques and actions are a part of the process of conscious creating, they are not the *cause* of the creations. The cause is the resonance you emit. The techniques and actions are merely a way to help you shift that resonance.

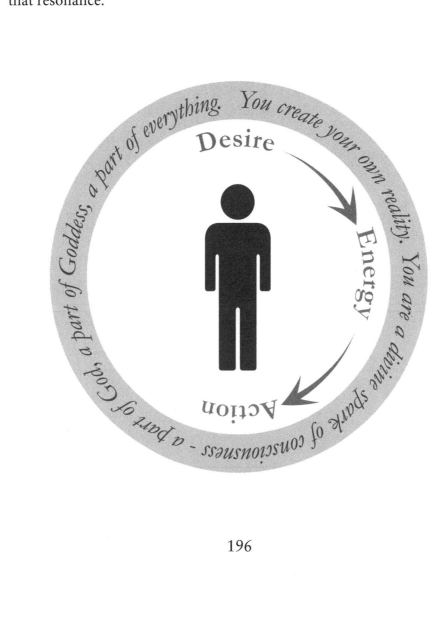

CREATION STEP *One*

WHAT DO YOU LOVE TO DO?

Make a list of 25 things you love to do.

- 1:

- 2:

- 3:

- 4:

- 5:

- 6:

- 7:

- 8:

- 9:

- 10:

- 11:

- 12:

13:

14:

15:

16:

17:

18:

19:

20:

21:

22:

23:

24:

25:

NOW, DO ONE OF THESE THINGS!

CREATION STEP ONE, CONT.

How did it feel to take action on something you enjoy?

Was this action easy for you, or hard?

Did you make any excuses to avoid taking the action you chose? Why?

{ extra writing space }

CREATION STEP *Two*

WHAT IS THE ESSENCE OF YOUR DESIRE?

Sit quietly and get in touch with the essence of one of your desires. Feel the joy and excitement. Imagine you could not fail. Ask: "What would be the most exciting and joyful next step?"

Write about your meditation in the space below.

Think about the next steps that came to you during the meditation. Can you take one or more of those steps right now?

Need more help
with taking action?
Go to page 230 of
The Map.

Once you've taken the action determined in the question above, write about how your dream feels now that you've taken action. What have you learned about your dream?

CREATION STEP *Three*

IF TAKING ACTION IS DIFFICULT FOR YOU …

If you don't feel inspired to take action toward your desire/intention, use the questions below to get to the root of your resistance.

MY DREAM/DESIRE: _____

_____

_____

_____

Is this really what I want?

Do I believe that I can create this?   Y   N   (if no, move on to the next question)

What beliefs are standing in my way?

(Once you've uncovered any limiting beliefs, change them using the tools in Chapter Six.)

Have I lost touch with the essence of my desire?

Look objectively at what your answers reveal. What needs to change in order to create alignment between your desire and your action?

What is your plan to change these things in order to create your dream?

PLAN:

RESULTS:

{ extra writing space }

CREATION STEP *Four*

JOY IN ACTION

Actions don't always have to be directly related to your dreams. Any action that brings you joy will flow energy towards more joy.

What would be the most exciting, fun thing to do right this minute?

What would be the most self-loving action you could take right now?

Every day for two weeks, do one thing that is "the most fun thing you can think of" to do. Keep track of your progress below or in your Creation Journal.

CREATION STEP *Five*

YOUR DREAM PLAN OF ACTION CHECKLIST

In this step, you'll prepare a plan of inspired action for at least one of your dreams.

MY DREAM/INTENTION:

ACTIONS TO TAKE/ TAKEN?

Action 1: _____

_____

_____

Action taken   Y   N   Date _____

Action 2: _____

_____

_____

Action taken   Y   N   Date _____

Action 3: _____

_____

_____

Action taken   Y   N   Date _____

Action 4: _____

_____

_____

Action taken   Y   N   Date _____

Action 5: _____

_____

_____

Action taken   Y   N   Date _____

CREATION STEP FIVE, CONT.

Action 6: _____

_____

_____

Action taken   Y   N   Date _____

Action 7: _____

_____

_____

Action taken   Y   N   Date _____

INTEND TO IMPLEMENT YOUR PLAN BY A CERTAIN DATE.

Write your intention below.

CHAPTER NINE

YOUR REALITY WILL RESPOND

"What you have thought all this time as Fairy Tales is actually the way life is."

- Bashar

Your world is always responding to you. Your personal reality is an absolute mirror, and it reflects exactly the energy you put out. This is why it is imperative to pay attention to how your reality responds to your shifts and changes as you begin to consciously create. If you don't pay attention, how will you know you are "flowing" energy that is in alignment with your desires?

With any powerful technique, you should see a sign within several days that will let you know it's working. When you are actively working on conscious creation, pay attention to everything in your world. Once you see the sign(s), expect that the full manifestation is going to happen! It's one thing to get excited about signs showing up, it's another to take it to the next level and truly expect your dream to manifest.

213

Share your successes only with people who will support you and your dream. Surround yourself with positive people, read books that solidify your knowing of conscious creation, and ask for help regularly from your unseen friends.

It may scare you when signs are negative. But you have everything you need in *The Map* to figure out why this is happening and change the beliefs that are causing your reality. If you don't believe that, make *that* your first belief to change.

Yes, sometimes it's a challenge to be patient. But with practice, you may not need patience at all, because when you truly feel as if you already have the thing you want, you will no longer be concerned about it manifesting. In your mind, you will already have it. When you are in that state, your dreams will become reality in the quickest, easiest, and most elegant way possible.

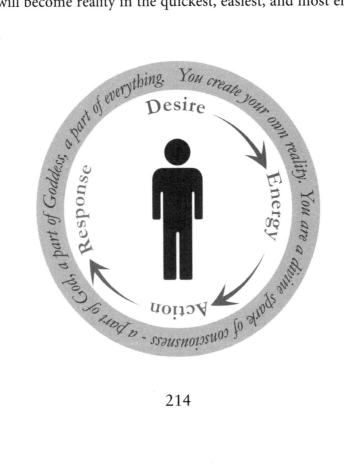

CREATION STEP *One*

OBSERVING THE SIGNS

Do one of the following techniques:

A DAY IN THE DAY OF THE DREAM

MAKING THE MOVIE REAL

GRATEFUL FOR NOW AND THEN

Note all signs that show up during the next seven days. Take notes in the space below. (If you don't receive a sign on a particular day, you can write your feelings about that, too.) Remember, no sign is too small to record!

DAY 1

TECHNIQUE DONE? _____

DATE _____   SIGN? Y   N

Describe the sign, how you recognized it, and how it made you feel.

Not sure what a sign looks like? Go to page 255 of *The Map.*

DAY 2   DATE _____   SIGN? Y N

Describe the sign, how you recognized it, and how it made you feel.

DAY 3   DATE _____   SIGN? Y N

Describe the sign, how you recognized it, and how it made you feel.

DAY 4   DATE _____   SIGN? Y N

Describe the sign, how you recognized it, and how it made you feel.

CREATION STEP ONE, CONT.

DAY 5   DATE _____   SIGN? Y N

Describe the sign, how you recognized it, and how it made you feel.

DAY 6   DATE _____   SIGN? Y N

Describe the sign, how you recognized it, and how it made you feel.

DAY 7   DATE _____   SIGN? Y N

Describe the sign, how you recognized it, and how it made you feel.

{ extra writing space }

CREATION STEP *Two*

ALIGNING YOUR REALITY

Review your notes from the seven days you spent in observation after doing your technique to increase the flow.

What were your responses to the signs you received?

Do these responses align with the reality you want to create?

How can you respond differently next time to create more of what
you desire?

CREATION STEP *Three*

SHIFT YOUR SELF-IMAGE

Work with your child and adolescent selves. Remind them that they don't have to live the success you desire, and then give them the reality they desire. Below, write all the reasons why *you* can handle this dream when it manifests.

{ extra writing space }

CREATION STEP *Four*

WORK WITH YOUR NEGATIVE SELF

Write out a conversation in which your negative self tells you all the reasons you can't handle the success of your dreams. When your negative self is finished, give it up to your higher self for healing.

{ extra writing space }

CREATION STEP *Five*

CHECK FOR SABOTAGING BELIEFS

Often, when you're on the alert for signs from your responsive Universe, negative or limiting beliefs you thought you'd shed can rear their ugly heads again—especially if you're not seeing the signs you were hoping for.

Write out any negative beliefs which have cropped up again. Then, change them using the techniques laid out for you in Chapter Six.

REMEMBER, you can purchase audio recordings of belief-changing meditations at LiveALifeYouLove.com.

{ extra writing space }

CHECK OUT
THE CONSCIOUS
CREATION STORIES AT
LiveALifeYouLove.com.
You can post your own
story there, too!

CHAPTER TEN

THE SECRET TO FASTER CHANGE

"Why bother to live an unhappy life?"

- Richard Bach

Okay, so you've discovered that you are the creator of your universe. You have written your intentions, and learned to flow positive energy toward those intentions every day. You've taken action toward your dreams and are watching carefully for signs that they're becoming manifest.

So ... What now?

Well, if you worked on your dream for half an hour each day, and did nothing during the other twenty-three-and-a-half hours but wait for your dream to manifest, everything would be cool. Your dream would manifest because nothing was opposing it. It would just be a matter of time.

But no one does that. We all have *thoughts* every day, and we have *emotions* with those thoughts.

Some of those thoughts and emotions aren't pretty. And if they're not pretty, they're stealing your dream.

If you follow The Map, you will get your dream. But The Map is not just a method to manifest your dreams: it's a way of life.

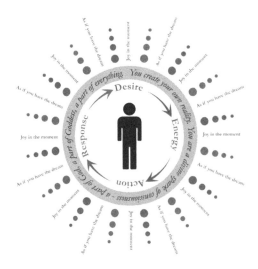

The secret to allowing the changes in your reality to take place in the quickest and most elegant way possible is this sixth step of The Map:

STAY IN JOY ...

AS IF YOU HAD THE DREAM!

Monitor the way you feel. Choose to be happy. And keep your resonance positive with the tools in this chapter.

CREATION STEP *One*

"NARROWING YOUR FOCUS" TECHNIQUE

For one full day, take stock of your mental state every hour. Ask yourself if you are focused on one—and only one—thing at a time. If not, do so. Notice how much more joy you can feel if you are not overwhelmed with a hundred things in your head at one time.

What was Narrowing Your Focus like for you?

{ more questions on the next page }

Need more info on this technique? Go to page 297 of *The Map*.

During what times/activities was it easy for you to focus on only one thing? When was it hard?

For how long were you able to maintain your single-pointed focus after each time you checked in?

At what points in your day did you feel most joyful?

CREATION STEP *Two*

REVISIT THE "DAY IN THE DAY OF THE DREAM"

Revisit the "Day in the Day of the Dream" technique—but this time, practice the "Narrowing Your Focus" technique at the same time. How did you experience your day differently this time? Was it easier to live the dream, or harder?

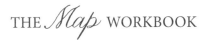

{ extra writing space }

CREATION STEP *Three*

WHAT MAKES YOU FEEL HAPPY?

Make a list of the things that make you feel happy. You can turn to this list when you need to shift your emotions back to happiness.

MY "HAPPY LIST"

1.

2.

3.

4.

5.

6.

7.

8.

9.

10.

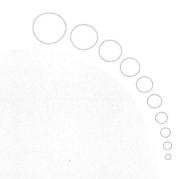

CREATION STEP *Four*

MAKE THE CHOICE

Happiness is a choice, not a condition. Don't wait until you have your dream to be happy—be happy NOW!

Most people have it ass-backwards. They think that things—including their dreams—are going to bring them happiness. But it's our *emotions* which create the realities of happiness or unhappiness. So be happy first, then dream your dreams, and be even happier!

DO YOU BELIEVE YOU CAN CHOOSE TO BE HAPPY?   Y   N

How do you feel about this statement? "*I am the creator of my own happiness?*"

What are you afraid might happen if you choose to be happy?

Do your fears reveal any beliefs which need to be changed? (For example, do you have a belief that says, "Circumstances create my happiness," or "I can be happy only if those I care about are happy?") If so, write that belief below, and change it using the tools you learned in Chapter Six.

OLD BELIEF: _____

NEW BELIEF: _____

BEING HAPPY DOESN'T MEAN IGNORING YOUR EMOTIONS! Find more information about letting your emotions flow on pages 292-294 of *The Map*.

CHAPTER ELEVEN

MAKE ROOM FOR MIRACLES

*"Be strong enough
to lean."*
- Lazaris

Every time you are stymied, you have the option to ask for assistance.

If you have trouble finding the root of a creation, ask your unseen friends to show you. If you have a repeating pattern that seems resistant to change, ask them to help you heal it. If you are unclear about how to state something in your intentions, ask them to guide you. If you have difficulty forgiving yourself or others, ask them to help you to forgive. Ask for help in discovering and changing your beliefs.

Whatever your desire, ask for help. It can't hurt, right? And it can be of tremendous benefit.

Don't expect to be perfect. Forgive yourself when you mess up. Creating your reality is supposed to be fun, remember?

You are in a partnership with your unseen friends. They want to help you, guide you, and assist you in lifting your resonance. They won't do it for you—this is a free-will universe—but your life can and will be easier as a result of working with them.

Miracles occur when we are given the help, realities, insights, and signs that we didn't ask for, didn't expect, and sometimes can't even imagine!

CREATION STEP

REQUEST FOR HELP FROM UNSEEN FRIENDS

Here is a sample request for help from your unseen friends.

> "*I call upon my higher self, my soul, my spirit, and all unseen friends who would love to assist me in the conscious creation of my personal heaven on earth. I ask for your support and assistance in manifesting all of my intentions with ease and elegance, in the perfect timing, and with harm to none.*
>
> "*I ask to become aware of any beliefs, habits, or thought patterns that stand in my way, and that the learning and growing that takes place be both gentle and loving.*
>
> "*I ask for your assistance in feeling my emotions fully as I read my intentions. I ask for you to help me recognize the little and big signs that will show the realities manifesting in my world.*
>
> "*I ask your assistance in helping me to manifest a dream even better than my intentions state, and I thank you in advance for your love and support.*"

In the space below, write out your own personal request. Read this request aloud any time you need help with your conscious creation.

{ more writing space on the next page }

Using the template on the next page, keep note of when you ask for help, and when you notice that help is being given.

CREATION STEP ONE, CONT.

DATE _____   HELP RECEIVED?   Y   N

Describe the help requested and received, how you recognized it, and how it made you feel.

DATE _____   HELP RECEIVED?   Y   N

Describe the help requested and received, how you recognized it, and how it made you feel.

DATE _____   HELP RECEIVED?   Y   N

Describe the help requested and received, how you recognized it, and how it made you feel.

DATE _____   HELP RECEIVED?   Y   N

Describe the help requested and received, how you recognized it, and how it made you feel.

DATE _____   HELP RECEIVED?   Y   N

Describe the help requested and received, how you recognized it, and how it made you feel.

DATE _____   HELP RECEIVED?   Y   N

Describe the help requested and received, how you recognized it, and how it made you feel.

CREATION STEP *Two*

FEEL THE GRATITUDE FOR YOUR UNSEEN HELPERS

Think about the times in your life when you knew you were guided, assisted, and loved by your unseen friends. Write a message of gratitude to your spirit helpers in the space below.

{ more writing space on the next page }

{ extra writing space }

CREATION STEP *Three*

MEET YOUR HIGHER SELF

Meditation is one way to meet and begin to know your higher self. Talk with your higher self about your dreams, your passions, and your joys. Let your higher self talk to you about their dreams for you.

Write about your experiences below.

If you'd prefer a recorded version of this technique, visit LiveALifeYouLove.com.

THE *Map* WORKBOOK

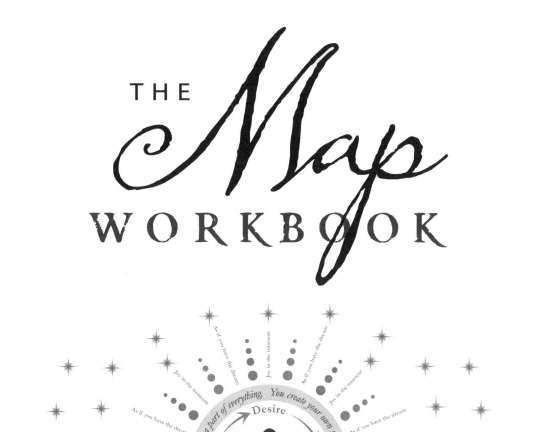

SECTION TWO

CREATION SESSIONS

CHAPTER TWELVE

CHANGE YOUR LIFE!

"You can either kiss the future or the past goodbye."

- Ringo Starr

The more effort you put into consciously creating your reality, the more your life will change. How you go about creating your dream life is up to you. There is no right way to approach conscious creation, and no wrong way. It is less about the specifics of what you *do*, and more about how it makes you *feel*.

HOW TO USE THESE
SAMPLE CREATION SESSIONS

Once you have read *The Map* and completed the exercises in Section One of this workbook, you will have some sweet successes under your belt. But you'll never stop dreaming! The sample Creation Sessions that follow are suggestions for working with new dreams. Use these sessions as a jumping-off point. Then, get creative, and design your own sessions that work perfectly for you!

249

You will know if you are on the right track with consciously creating your reality if you are excited, focused, motivated—and most of all, having fun!

You will find that it sometimes feels right to move forward quickly, and at other times it feels right to slow down, wait for a sign, and take time to integrate changes you've made (like altering your beliefs).

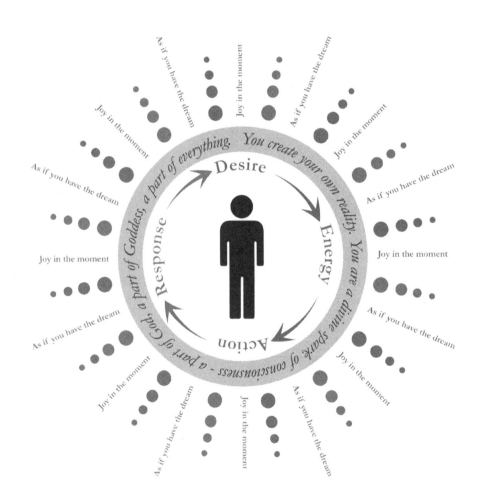

CREATION SESSION *One*

PREPARE YOUR SACRED CREATING SPACE. Light a candle, play some soft music, turn down the lights, and ready your mind and heart for this time of consciously creating your reality.

INVITE YOUR HIGHER SELF TO ASSIST YOU.

> *"Dear Higher Self, please help me with the work I am about to do. I ask for your help with my dream and the process of manifesting it. I ask for your assistance with clarity, insight, trust, and focus. Thank you."*

You can also write your own call for assistance. Use the space provided at the end of this section, or write in your Creation Journal.

WRITE OUT OR UPDATE YOUR INTENTIONS. Include your immediate intentions. Then, read them aloud, and really feel the impact they have on your emotional body. Imagine the impact they will have on your life when they come into being.

DO THE "BLENDING WITH YOUR HIGHER SELF" TECHNIQUE. You can find this technique in Chapter Three. Write about your experience in the space provided at the end of this section or in your Creation Journal.

CHOOSE AN AREA OF YOUR LIFE TO FOCUS ON FOR THE NEXT SEVEN DAYS. This focus could be around a new dream or a dream you've been dreaming for a while. Reread your intentions for this dream. Assess whether you would like to add to them or change them in any way. Make sure they fully state what you would like to create and that you are excited and expectant that this dream will manifest.

DO THE "IGNITING YOUR INTENTIONS" TECHNIQUE. You can find this technique in Chapter Seven. Write about your experience in the space provided at the end of this section or in your Creation Journal.

SAY THE "CLOSING WITH GRATITUDE STATEMENT."

> *"Dear Higher Self, thank you for your assistance this day. I ask that you continue to assist me, and gently help me to be aware of my thoughts, discover my beliefs, recognize my patterns, and stay in joy, this day and every day. Thank you."*

You can also write your own closing gratitude statement. Use the space provided at the end of this section, or write in your Creation Journal.

STAY IN JOY. For the rest of the day, stay in joy as much as you possibly can. Note your success or challenges with this.

SAMPLE CREATION SESSION ONE, CONT.

{ Writing Space }

SAMPLE CREATION SESSION ONE, CONT.

{ Writing Space }

SAMPLE CREATION SESSION ONE, CONT.

{ Writing Space }

SAMPLE CREATION SESSION ONE, CONT.

{ Writing Space }

CREATION SESSION *Two*

PREPARE YOUR SACRED CREATING SPACE. Light a candle, play some soft music, turn down the lights, and ready your mind and heart for this time of consciously creating your reality.

INVITE YOUR HIGHER SELF TO ASSIST YOU.

"Dear Higher Self, please help me with the work I am about to do. I ask for your help with my dream and the process of manifesting it. I ask for your assistance with clarity, insight, trust, and focus. Thank you."

You can also write your own call for assistance. Use the space provided at the end of this section, or write in your Creation Journal.

READ YOUR INTENTIONS (OR WRITE OUT NEW ONES). Feel as much excitement as possible about creating your dream life. Focus on your Overall Intention and the Core Intentions that outline your primary dream.

WORK WITH YOUR FLOW-STOPPERS. Revisit the section on Flow-Stoppers (Chapter Five). Do you habitually feel any of these emotions around your primary dream? If so, revisit the exercises in this workbook to clear those emotions.

DO THE "DAY IN THE DAY OF THE DREAM" TECHNIQUE. You can find this technique in Chapter Seven. Write about your experience in the space provided at the end of this section or in your Creation Journal.

REFLECT ON YOUR ABILITY TO REMAIN IN JOY. Reflect on the past twenty-four hours and your ability to remain in a state of joy. On a scale of one to ten (ten being the most joyful), how would you rate yourself?

1   2   3   4   5   6   7   8   9   10

What can you do differently tomorrow?

REFLECT ON THE SIGNS YOU'VE RECEIVED. Think about the past few days. What signs have you received to indicate that you are moving toward manifesting your dream? (Refer to Chapter Nine if you need a refresher.)

SAY THE "CLOSING WITH GRATITUDE STATEMENT."

"Dear Higher Self, thank you for your assistance this day. I ask that you continue to assist me, and gently help me to be aware of my thoughts, discover my beliefs, recognize my patterns, and stay in joy, this day and every day. Thank you."

You can also write your own closing gratitude statement. Use the space provided at the end of this section, or write in your Creation Journal.

STAY IN JOY. For the rest of the day, stay in joy as much as you possibly can. Note your success or challenges with this.

SAMPLE CREATION SESSION TWO, CONT.

{ Writing Space }

{ Writing Space }

SAMPLE CREATION SESSION TWO, CONT.

{ Writing Space }

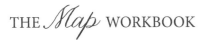

SAMPLE CREATION SESSION TWO, CONT.

{ Writing Space }

CREATION SESSION *Three*

PREPARE YOUR SACRED CREATING SPACE. Light a candle, play some soft music, turn down the lights, and ready your mind and heart for this time of consciously creating your reality.

INVITE YOUR HIGHER SELF TO ASSIST YOU.

> *"Dear Higher Self, please help me with the work I am about to do. I ask for your help with my dream and the process of manifesting it. I ask for your assistance with clarity, insight, trust, and focus. Thank you."*

You can also write your own call for assistance. Use the space provided at the end of this section, or write in your Creation Journal.

VISIT YOUR CHILD SELF, ADOLESCENT SELF, AND YOUNG ADULT SELVES IN A VISUALIZATION. Tell them what you are planning to create (your primary dream). Ask them how they feel about it, and write about their feelings at the end of this section. (If you need a refresher, go to Chapter Five.)

READ THE LETTER FROM YOUR FUTURE SELF in Appendix B of *The Map*, or use it as an example to write your own. (You can use the space provided at the end of this section, or write in your Creation Journal.) Imagine being there, and being that person. How are they different from you, especially emotionally? How do they move through their day? How easily do they laugh, play, and have fun?

REFLECT ON YOUR ABILITY TO REMAIN PRESENT. Reflect on the past twenty-four hours and your ability to remain in the present moment. On a scale of one to ten, how would you rate yourself?

1   2   3   4   5   6   7   8   9   10

REFLECT ON THE SIGNS YOU'VE RECEIVED. Think about the past few days. What signs have you received to indicate that you are moving toward manifesting your dream? (Refer to Chapter Nine if you need a refresher.)

SAY THE "CLOSING WITH GRATITUDE STATEMENT."

> *"Dear Higher Self, thank you for your assistance this day. I ask that you continue to assist me, and gently help me to be aware of my thoughts, discover my beliefs, recognize my patterns, and stay in joy, this day and every day. Thank you."*

You can also write your own closing gratitude statement. Use the space provided at the end of this section, or write in your Creation Journal.

STAY IN JOY. For the rest of the day, stay in joy as much as you possibly can. Note your success or challenges with this.

SAMPLE CREATION SESSION THREE, CONT.

{ Writing Space }

SAMPLE CREATION SESSION THREE, CONT.

{ Writing Space }

SAMPLE CREATION SESSION THREE, CONT.

{ Writing Space }

SAMPLE CREATION SESSION THREE, CONT.

{ Writing Space }

CREATION SESSION *Four*

PREPARE YOUR SACRED CREATING SPACE. Light a candle, play some soft music, turn down the lights, and ready your mind and heart for this time of consciously creating your reality.

INVITE YOUR HIGHER SELF TO ASSIST YOU.

"Dear Higher Self, please help me with the work I am about to do. I ask for your help with my dream and the process of manifesting it. I ask for your assistance with clarity, insight, trust, and focus. Thank you."

You can also write your own call for assistance. Use the space provided at the end of this section, or write in your Creation Journal.

READ YOUR INTENTIONS ALOUD (ESPECIALLY THOSE AROUND YOUR PRIMARY DREAM THIS WEEK). Feel as much excitement about them as possible.

THINK ABOUT THE DREAM YOU ARE FOCUSED ON CREATING RIGHT NOW. Write about your history in this area of your life (e.g., your history with men/women if your primary dream has to do with a relationship, or your history with money, health, career, etc.) Has anything happened in your past around this issue that you still feel strong emotion about? If yes, write a "Hate Letter" to release the emotion (see Chapter Six). Or work with the younger adult "you" who was disappointed in the past. Write the results of this exercise in the space provided at the end of this section, or in your Creation Journal.

DO THE "MAKING THE MOVIE REAL" TECHNIQUE (CHAPTER SEVEN). Write about the results of this in the space provided at the end of this section, or in your Creation Journal.

REFLECT ON YOUR ABILITY TO HOLD THE RESONANCE OF YOUR DREAM. On a scale of one to ten, how would you rate yourself?

1   2   3   4   5   6   7   8   9   10

What will you do differently tomorrow?

REFLECT ON THE SIGNS YOU'VE RECEIVED. Think about the past few days. What signs have you received to indicate that you are moving toward manifesting your dream? (Refer to Chapter Nine if you need a refresher.)

SAY THE "CLOSING WITH GRATITUDE STATEMENT."

> *"Dear Higher Self, thank you for your assistance this day. I ask that you continue to assist me, and gently help me to be aware of my thoughts, discover my beliefs, and recognize my patterns and to stay in joy this day and every day. Thank you."*

You can also write your own closing gratitude statement. Use the space provided at the end of this section, or write in your Creation Journal.

STAY IN JOY. For the rest of the day, stay in joy as much as you possibly can. Note your success or challenges with this.

SAMPLE CREATION SESSION FOUR, CONT.

{ Writing Space }

THE *Map* WORKBOOK

{ Writing Space }

SAMPLE CREATION SESSION FOUR, CONT.

{ Writing Space }

{ Writing Space }

CREATION SESSION *Five*

PREPARE YOUR SACRED CREATING SPACE. Light a candle, play some soft music, turn down the lights, and ready your mind and heart for this time of consciously creating your reality.

INVITE YOUR HIGHER SELF TO ASSIST YOU.

> *"Dear Higher Self, please help me with the work I am about to do. I ask for your help with my dream and the process of manifesting it. I ask for your assistance with clarity, insight, trust, and focus. Thank you."*

You can also write your own call for assistance. Use the space provided at the end of this section, or write in your Creation Journal.

READ YOUR INTENTIONS ALOUD (ESPECIALLY THOSE AROUND YOUR PRIMARY DREAM THIS WEEK). Feel as much excitement about them as possible.

VISUALIZE SITTING WITH YOUR NEGATIVE SELF. Tell it what you intend to create in the area of your primary dream. Let it tell you how impossible that is. How idiotic. How stupid. How you will fail. What a ridiculous idea that is. Let it rant and rave, and when it finally pauses, ask it if it is complete. It will not be. Let it tear into you about other areas of your life as well. Let it drone on and on, dumping all of its venom. And when it is complete, call your higher self to take your negative self away for healing. Feel the freedom.

DO THE "GRATEFUL FOR NOW AND THEN" TECHNIQUE (CHAPTER SEVEN). Write about the results of this in the space provided at the end of this section, or in your Creation Journal.

REFLECT ON YOUR ABILITY TO LIVE AS IF YOU ALREADY HAVE THE DREAM. On a scale of one to ten, how would you rate yourself?

1   2   3   4   5   6   7   8   9   10

What will you do differently tomorrow?

REFLECT ON THE SIGNS YOU'VE RECEIVED. Think about the past few days. What signs have you received to indicate that you are moving toward manifesting your dream? (Refer to Chapter Nine if you need a refresher.)

SAY THE "CLOSING WITH GRATITUDE STATEMENT."

"Dear Higher Self, thank you for your assistance this day. I ask that you continue to assist me, and gently help me to be aware of my thoughts, discover my beliefs, recognize my patterns, and stay in joy, this day and every day. Thank you."

You can also write your own closing gratitude statement. Use the space provided at the end of this section, or write in your Creation Journal.

STAY IN JOY. For the rest of the day, stay in joy as much as you possibly can. Note your success or challenges with this.

SAMPLE CREATION SESSION FIVE, CONT.

{ Writing Space }

SAMPLE CREATION SESSION FIVE, CONT.

{ Writing Space }

SAMPLE CREATION SESSION FIVE, CONT.

{ Writing Space }

{ Writing Space }

CREATION SESSION *Six*

PREPARE YOUR SACRED CREATING SPACE. Light a candle, play some soft music, turn down the lights, and ready your mind and heart for this time of consciously creating your reality.

INVITE YOUR HIGHER SELF TO ASSIST YOU.

> *"Dear Higher Self, please help me with the work I am about to do. I ask for your help with my dream and the process of manifesting it. I ask for your assistance with clarity, insight, trust, and focus. Thank you."*

You can also write your own call for assistance. Use the space provided at the end of this section, or write in your Creation Journal.

READ YOUR INTENTIONS ALOUD (ESPECIALLY THOSE AROUND YOUR PRIMARY DREAM THIS WEEK). Feel as much excitement about them as possible.

GO OVER YOUR NOTES FROM OTHER CREATION SESSIONS, AND YOUR NOTES FROM YOUR TIME WITH YOUR CHILD, ADOLESCENT, AND YOUNG ADULT SELVES. Make a list of beliefs that need to change, and the new beliefs you want to change them to.

WRITE OUT AN ACTION PLAN FOR YOUR CURRENT DREAM (SEE CHAPTER EIGHT). You can also use the writing space at the end of this section, or write in your Creation Journal.

REFLECT ON YOUR ABILITY TO LIVE IN JOY, STAY IN THE MOMENT, AND FEEL AS IF YOU ALREADY HAVE THE DREAM. On a scale of one to ten, how would you rate yourself?

1   2   3   4   5   6   7   8   9   10

What will you do differently tomorrow?

REFLECT ON THE SIGNS YOU'VE RECEIVED. Think about the past few days. What signs have you received to indicate that you are moving toward manifesting your dream? (Refer to Chapter Nine if you need a refresher.)

SAY THE "CLOSING WITH GRATITUDE STATEMENT."

> *"Dear Higher Self, thank you for your assistance this day. I ask that you continue to assist me, and gently help me to be aware of my thoughts, discover my beliefs, recognize my patterns, and stay in joy, this day and every day. Thank you."*

You can also write your own closing gratitude statement. Use the space provided at the end of this section, or write in your Creation Journal.

STAY IN JOY. For the rest of the day, stay in joy as much as you possibly can. Note your success or challenges with this.

SAMPLE CREATION SESSION SIX, CONT.

{ Writing Space }

{ Writing Space }

SAMPLE CREATION SESSION SIX, CONT.

{ Writing Space }

SAMPLE CREATION SESSION SIX, CONT.

{ Writing Space }

CREATION SESSION *Seven*

PREPARE YOUR SACRED CREATING SPACE. Light a candle, play some soft music, turn down the lights, and ready your mind and heart for this time of consciously creating your reality.

INVITE YOUR HIGHER SELF TO ASSIST YOU.

> *"Dear Higher Self, please help me with the work I am about to do. I ask for your help with my dream and the process of manifesting it. I ask for your assistance with clarity, insight, trust, and focus. Thank you."*

You can also write your own call for assistance. Use the space provided at the end of this section, or write in your Creation Journal.

READ YOUR INTENTIONS ALOUD (ESPECIALLY THOSE AROUND YOUR PRIMARY DREAM THIS WEEK). Feel as much excitement about them as possible.

DO THE "YOUR NURTURING UNIVERSE" TECHNIQUE (CHAPTER THREE). Write about the results of this in the space provided at the end of this section, or in your Creation Journal.

CHANGE THE BELIEFS YOU PREPARED IN CREATION SESSION SIX. Write out the new beliefs and post them in your bathroom, bedroom, or kitchen so you can read them whenever you see them (with joy, gratitude, and excitement please)!

MAKE A LIST OF THINGS THAT WILL HELP YOU STAY IN JOY IF YOU SLIP OUT TEMPORARILY (CHAPTER ELEVEN). Write about the results of this in the space provided at the end of this section, or in your Creation Journal.

REFLECT ON THE SIGNS YOU'VE RECEIVED. Think about the past few days. What signs have you received to indicate that you are moving toward manifesting your dream? (Refer to Chapter Nine if you need a refresher.)

SAY THE "CLOSING WITH GRATITUDE STATEMENT."

"Dear Higher Self, thank you for your assistance this day. I ask that you continue to assist me, and gently help me to be aware of my thoughts, discover my beliefs, recognize my patterns, and stay in joy, this day and every day. Thank you."

You can also write your own closing gratitude statement. Use the space provided at the end of this section, or write in your Creation Journal.

STAY IN JOY. You know what to do …

SAMPLE CREATION SESSION SEVEN, CONT.

{ Writing Space }

{ Writing Space }

SAMPLE CREATION SESSION SEVEN, CONT.

{ Writing Space }

THE *Map* WORKBOOK

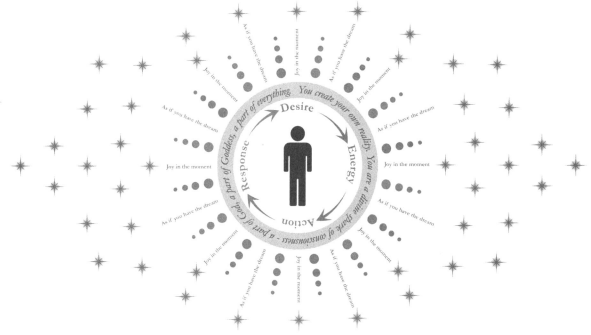

SECTION THREE
TROUBLESHOOTING

CHAPTER THIRTEEN

TROUBLESHOOTING YOUR REALITY

*"Problems are not
stop signs, they are
guidelines."*

- Robert H. Schuller

Sometimes, despite your best efforts, a dream may not manifest as quickly as you'd like ... or at all. Here is a sample creation session for when your dream doesn't manifest as planned.

MANIFESTATION QUESTIONNAIRE

WRITE YOUR INTENTION FOR YOUR DREAM HERE:

What have you been thinking and feeling (on a day to day basis) around this issue?

Are your intentions crystal clear about all aspects of the thing you desire? If not, clarify them. (If you are unsure, find someone to work with you on this issue.) Write your new intentions in the space below.

Have you stopped flowing negative energy (Chapter Five)? Check in to make sure you're not grappling with Flow-Stopper emotions.

Have you been proactive about flowing positive energy? Have you been doing regular (at minimum once a week) techniques to flow positive energy towards your dream? If no, why not?

Have you taken inspired action (Chapter Eight)? If no, why not?

Although there are no absolute timetables to consult, with practice you will begin to get a feel for where you are in the manifestation process. Bigger dreams take longer. Have you been patient enough to allow the new dream to manifest? How do you feel about this process of patience?

Have you been watching for signs? All dreams respond with signs when a powerful technique is implemented, but you won't see the signs if you aren't looking. Write your feelings about signs and your experience with them with regard to this dream.

Is there something/someone you need to forgive? If so, release your emotions. Forgive, or get some help in forgiving. Sometimes professional help is appropriate and a godsend. Intend to forgive and/or seek the assistance and accept the help. Write about your forgiveness process.

Finally, if you don't find the reason for the miscreation anywhere else, delve deeply into your beliefs (Chapters Five and Six.)

WHAT'S THAT? YOU'RE CERTAIN NONE OF THESE SUGGESTIONS APPLY TO YOU?

Then, my friend, I suggest professional assistance. Sometimes (very, very rarely), there is a deep-rooted cause for the energies we flow. But there is always, repeat, *always* a reason for every reality. No one is an exception to the truth that we create our own reality. Ask to be guided to the perfect person to help you through this dark place.

YOU *CAN* CREATE WHAT YOU DESIRE. HAVE FAITH IN THE PROCESS, DO YOUR WORK, AND LET THE MAP GUIDE YOU!

AFTERWORD

SHARE YOUR CREATION

I would love to hear from you! E-mail your successes, questions, and comments to BoniLonnsburry@LiveALifeYouLove.com.

You can also find stories from other conscious creators, audio recordings of the meditations and exercises in this workbook, and tons of other resources on my web site, www.LiveALifeYouLove.com.

ACKNOWLEDGMENTS

I would like to extend my sincere and heartfelt gratitude to my readers. You make my job so much fun and immensely rewarding. I'm proud and honored that you have taken my advice and ran with it—creating jobs, money, love, and successes of all types. You make me excited to keep writing and creating.

I also am deeply grateful for Bryna René, without whom this book would not exist. Bryna's fabulous writing and editorial skills—along with her beautiful graphics throughout the book—made this book what it is. She not only created this entire book with elegance and grace, but was also an absolute joy to work with.

And to Richard, I send my heartfelt appreciation—not only for his ongoing support and love, but also for his belief in me and my work.

ABOUT THE AUTHOR

BONI LONNSBURRY

Boni Lonnsburry is the CVO (Chief Visionary Officer) of Inner Art Inc., an expert on conscious creation, and the author of the best-selling, award-winning book, *The Map: To Our Responsive Universe, Where Dreams Really Do Come True*, winner of seven book awards including the prestigious Nautilus Award.

Boni has an undergraduate degree in business, and was pursuing a joint law and MBA degree when she realized it wasn't her bliss. She quit both schools and began the search to find the work she loved.

Jobless in 2000, Boni invested $50 and incorporated a marketing company, In Touch Today. In only five years, without further financing, the company was grossing $5 million in annual sales, and Boni had transformed her financial life from bankruptcy to abundance beyond her wildest dreams.

Boni also consciously created the "love of her life" at an age when most people have given up hope. She and her husband, Richard, were married in Fiji in 2010 and together have nine children and eleven grandchildren. They split their time between homes in the Bahamas and Boulder, Colorado.

In her free time, Boni enjoys reading, snorkeling, traveling, hiking, meditating, and conversing with her unseen friends.

Boni believes each of us is on the planet to create a life we love, then help others do the same—and, finally, create a world we love to live in. Her website, www.LiveALifeYouLove.com, is dedicated to providing information on how to accomplish precisely that.